Bermuda
Her Plants and Gardens
1609–1850

Jill Collett

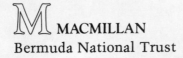
MACMILLAN
Bermuda National Trust

First published 1987

Published by
Macmillan Publishers Ltd and
the *Bermuda National Trust*
London and Basingstoke
*Associated companies and representatives in Accra,
Auckland, Delhi, Dublin, Gaborone, Hamburg, Harare,
Hong Kong, Kuala Lumpur, Lagos, Manzini, Melbourne,
Mexico City, Nairobi, New York, Singapore, Tokyo*

ISBN 0-333-43784-5

Printed in Hong Kong

British Library Cataloguing in Publication Data
Collett, Jill
   Bermuda: her plants and gardens 1609-1850.
   1. Plants, Ornamental—Bermuda—History
   I. Title II. Bermuda National Trust
   635.9′ 097299   SB404.6.B46
ISBN 0-333-43784-5

To Isadore whose idea it was.

Contents

Introduction

This book is my present to Bermuda. It is a thank you for having had the opportunity to develop what will be a lifelong interest.

It all started in 1977 when Paul Miles, then the Horticulturist to the National Trust in England, came to Bermuda and gave a lecture to the Bermuda National Trust on the restoration of gardens to provide an appropriate setting for old houses. The idea was to grow only those plants that would have been used in such gardens within one hundred years of the house having been built. The shape of the garden was also of importance. Hundreds of ornamental plants grow in Bermuda today but very few importations had been documented. We had to have a better list.

Work was begun by the then Archivist, Len McDonald, and the Horticultural Officer, Andrew Pierce, and J. Hubert Jones of the Department of Agriculture, on trying to find out what plants were imported, and when. They produced a short list but it was by no means adequate for the purpose. It was from there that I started. I very soon realised that no work of mine could surpass that of Major-General Sir J.H. Lefroy who wrote a chapter 'Botany' in *The Natural History of Bermuda* edited by J.M. Jones, 1884, giving a comprehensive list of plants then growing, or of N.L. Britton who wrote Bermuda's only complete *Flora* in 1918. They must stand as authorities until someone with the knowledge and ability can improve on their work. I decided to confine myself to the years 1609–1850 because it was that period which had not really been researched before. Major-General Lefroy has something relevant to say on the subject.

It gives much interest to the early accounts that they throw incidental light on the original productions of the group [of islands]and enable us to account with certainty for the introduction of many species which are not naturalised, but which might, in the absence of information, have been taken to be native. It is a curious fact that almost everything cultivated in Bermuda is, and apparently always has been, grown from imported seed — seed from England, from America, from Madeira and the West Indies — necessarily disseminating also weeds and chance species, which naturalise themselves with great facility.

The research has been a fascinating occupation. It has taken me to several libraries abroad where I have always received a great deal of help on Bermuda's behalf. In order to understand the importation of plants to this island it was necessary to learn about the discovery of plants, where they originated, who discovered them, and the history of the voyages of discovery. Englishmen were by no means the only ones setting forth on these plant collecting expeditions.

In the early years of the colony most plants had a local and commercial use and it was only in the eighteenth century that the imports of purely ornamental plants started. Any new colony was established as a primarily commercial venture and all plants grown had to have some use; considerations of beauty came with long establishment and leisure. It became obvious as my research continued that I was amassing as much information about agriculture as about plant importation. It also became obvious that by the standards of past centuries Bermuda was no more isolated than many another place. In fact I consider what happened in Bermuda to be similar to other colonies — so many of the same plants were being experimented with for trading purposes. We know that tastes in clothes and furniture were contemperaneous with those in America and the islands of the West Indies but it has become obvious that many plants arrived here soon after they were first discovered elsewhere. This is perfectly understandable when it is realised how far and wide Bermuda vessels sailed: to the West Indian islands; the coasts of South America and all up the eastern coast of North America and Canada; to England; to Africa; round the Cape and possibly as far as China. Naturally men saw what was done in other places with plants and thought it worth trying the ideas here. One example of this is the Barbados Flower Fence (*Caesalpinia pulcherrima*) used in exactly the way its name suggests. In Bermuda the Tucker family tried it.

The mentions of Bermuda are sparse in many books and libraries. I think this is not only due to the fact that Bermuda is so small, it is due to the fact that so much else was going on at the same time. For instance Bermuda and Virginia were settled at the same time and the West Indian islands soon after. When ships sailed north and south they might call at Bermuda for water, potatoes, onions or other produce but it was a destination in itself only for Bermuda-owned vessels. In the eighteenth century Bermuda was just one of many island possessions. Nevertheless throughout the period 1609–1850 its plants and productions have been noted as of interest. It is hard for us now to realise the enormous interest there was in the seventeenth and eighteenth centuries about all the new plants that were being discovered and how and if they had a commercial value.

'Exoticks' had been grown in Europe since the sixteenth century. The first modern Botanic Garden was established in Padua in the middle of the same century, closely followed by others. (The ancient Greeks and Mexicans had Botanic Gardens.) The purpose of these gardens was for display and study and the beds were so arranged that the plants could be viewed from all sides. When one remembers that most medicine and many dyes came from plants and that spices and herbs enlivened the contemporary food it is all the more explicable. Most men who regarded themselves as educated had an interest in botany and most Governors of Bermuda seem to have been charged with endeavouring to make the place productive — in the early years for the profit of investors, later on so that the islands could be self-sufficient and defensible. There was a great deal of traffic in plants going in both directions between England and America. There was a select body of men who were renowned botanists in their day all writing to each other and exchanging seeds, plants and information. It is among the writings and collections of men such as James Petiver, Mark Catesby, John Lawson and Dr Fothergill that Bermuda's name appears.

John Dickinson, who may have built Verdmont, Smith's Parish, at the end of the seventeenth century sent the first collections of plants from Bermuda to James Petiver in about 1700. Those plants came into the possession of Sir Hans Sloane and became part of the present-day Sloane Herbarium in the Natural History Museum, South Kensington, London. Dickinson obviously corresponded at some length with Petiver and we have three of his letters about his collections. He also offered to obtain plants from 'Campeche and the Bahamas' for Petiver.

Mark Catesby wrote the first natural history of America, *Natural History of Carolina, Florida and the Bahama Islands*. He too was an acquaintance of Petiver. In his beautifully illustrated book he mentions the palmetto and the plait made from it in such a way that it sounds as if he came to Bermuda sometime in the 1720s to observe for himself, for he mentions bluebirds and Bermuda potatoes as well.

John Lawson published a book in 1701 entitled *A New Voyage to Carolina*. He describes how the Bermudians traded with Carolina, the 'beer' made of cedar berries and the angel fish.

Dr Fothergill was part of the eighteenth century circle of botanists. He particularly wanted to collect American plants and became patron and friend to several men and corresponded regularly with America. It is from him that we have confirmation of the second collection of plants from Bermuda in about 1734 by Revd William Clerk. These are now at Oxford University. The manner in which Bermuda is mentioned by these men makes it perfectly obvious that they considered the island no more remote than anywhere else and they expected their readers to know where it was, which is slightly different from present-day circumstances.

Acknowledgements

The inspiration for this book came from Mrs A.W. Smith who, long before I dreamed that it was possible that I could collect enough information, talked in terms of 'your book'. Her two books *Early American Gardens* and *American Gardens in the Eighteenth Century*, published under her pen name of Ann Leighton, have been both an inspiration and an unfailing source of information for me, because I realised that as the ties between Bermuda, Virginia and the eastern seaboard have always been close and strong, what was growing there at any given time might well have been growing here too.

Mr W. Zuill of the Bermuda National Trust has been a kind and supportive friend, showing interest in a subject of which he knew nothing when I first started. Mrs Lorna Mercer has also been a good, kind, listening friend to whom I expounded my ideas and theories. My own family willy-nilly have learned more about garden history than they ever thought was possible. They have visited libraries and gardens with me, given me books and encouragement, understood about the time needed for the project and, above all, always believed that the book would really be published.

I would like to thank Miss Helen Rowe of the Bermuda Archives, the staff of the Reference Library and Mrs Penny Hill and Miss Debbie Monkman of the Department of Agriculture Library in Bermuda for all their help and assistance. Mr Andrew Trimingham has allowed me to have the rarely-seen Van der Aa map of 1720 from his collection copied for this book and my thanks go to him and to Mr Mark Emmerson for doing the necessary work. Miss Sylvia Fitzgerald of Kew Library gave me a lot of her time and showed kind interest in my project, as did Miss Judy Weinberg of the Massachusetts Horticultural Library. I have visited the Library of the Natural History Museum, South Kensington, London, the British Museum, The Bodleian Library, Oxford, the Linnean Rooms, London, the Asa Gray Herbarium and the Houghton Library at Harvard, the Essex Institute at Cambridge, Massachusetts, and always I have received the greatest possible help from their staff. I would like to thank Mr W. Zuill also for reading the manuscript and to thank Mr J. Hubert Jones for doing the same and offering so many constructive suggestions which I am sure have contributed to clarity in the text. The Camera Store staff have always been unfailingly helpful with suggestions about my photography.

Major-General Sir J.H. Lefroy's work *Memorials of the Bermudas* is a magnificent source of information on the early years of the colony and I have referred to it many times. The publication of *The Rich Papers* edited by Vernon Ives has also been invaluable for further information about the early years. N.L. Britton's work *Flora of Bermuda* is a very useful reference book; no other book of such complete coverage of plant life in Bermuda has been written before or since. Mrs L.H. Smith's book *Bermuda's Oldest Inhabitants* has been of great help and of particular value are the stories that are told nowhere else and should not be lost.

All Latin names are those used in *Hortus* except where [Britton] appears which indicates it is his *Flora* that has supplied the name. It must be remembered that rather long Latin names were used in the sixteenth and seventeenth centuries by herbalists and botanists but names for plants were not systematized until the eighteenth century by Carl Linnaeus. Until then the educated layman used the popular or common names in his correspondence and accounts. A full bibliography appears at the end of the book.

If I appear to repeat myself on occasions it is to help the reader who may only be interested in one aspect of the book and who has not read the other chapters.

Photographic acknowledgements

Photograph of Francois André Michaux, page 19. Copyright of The Trustees of the Royal Botanic Gardens, Kew © 1986; Reproduced with permission.

All other photographs by the author, Jill Collett.

The line drawings in the Farming chapter are based on drawings from Gerard's *Herbal* of 1633.

Farming

The history of agriculture in Bermuda varies from success to decline and back to success again. At the time of the founding of the colony all colonies were intended to make the fortunes of their sponsors. The ships that sailed for the New World were equipped with everything for a new life and that included tools for ship and housebuilding and farming, plus the seeds to grow food both for immediate use and for cash crops. It was also

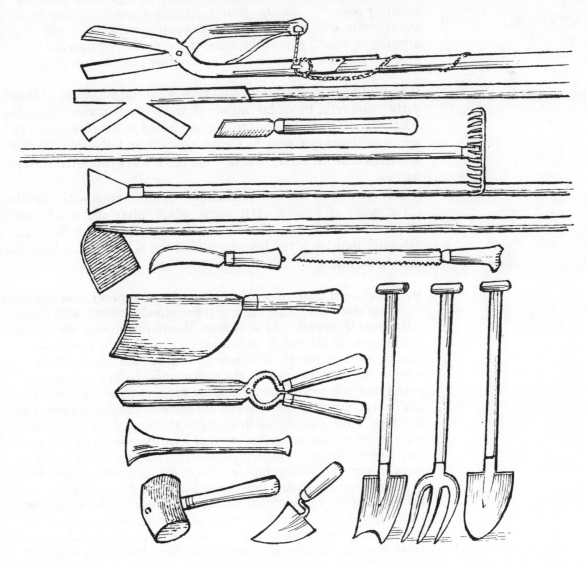

necessary to carry stores on which to live until the crops could be harvested. When the *Sea Venture* was wrecked the bounty of the islands provided food for those first months. The sea stores rescued from the wreck were available for the onward voyage to Virginia where they saved the lives of the starving remnant of the settlers there. Two ships were built for that voyage, the *Patience* and the *Deliverance*.

It is interesting to read the account of Captain Diego Ramirez, a Spanish captain wrecked in 1603, as it tells us what the islands were like at that time and adds to our knowledge of what the colonists found in 1609.

All island covered with cedar forests and tufted palmetto and other underbrush of various varieties ... good timber for vessels ... and lumber of all sorts in abundance ... Plenty of pigs, worn paths to watering places .... Little grass ... thinly wooded ... easy to travel about. On the extremity of the point some tobacco was growing as though planted by man for there was nothing else growing there nor was this seen in any other place except there.

It should be explained here that nearly all the accounts of those early years refer to 'cedar' although the writers obviously meant what we call *Juniperus bermudiana*. Gerard in his *Herbal* of 1595 refers to 'Prickly Cedar or Cedar juniper' and also has 'Juniper and his kinds'. It seems the layman has always muddled the two names.

The fertility of the soil had become obvious even with the first three years of human settlement when, after the newly-built ships sailed away to Virginia, two men remained on Bermuda. Silvester Jourdan gives his account of the return to see how the men were faring.

We found them civil, honest and religious ... for they have planted ... great store of wheate, beanes, tobacco and mellons, with many other good things for the use of man. Illustrating further the interest and pleasure of discovery, he continues: *For the fruits which the land yields, they bee the Mulberie great store, and peares which have in them a red liquor, as the pomegranate hath, or somewhat redder, but very wholesome if you eat an hundred at one time, you shall never surfeit of them, if you eat some proportion of them they will bind, but if you exceed in eating of them, then are they of the contrary operation, yet never any that hurt themselves by them eat they never so many. It is certaine that one man eat above a peck of them in some ten houres and was never the worse. We have a kind of Berrie upon the Cedar tree, verie pleasant to eat and for the Palmito tree the toppe of it is a great deale sweeter and wholesomer then any Cabedge. In some of our Islands there growes pepper, but not so good as our Indian pepper, divers sorts of other good things there is which the severall times of the yeare bring forth one after*

† 2 *Sana Sancta Indorum.*
Tabaco of Trinidada.

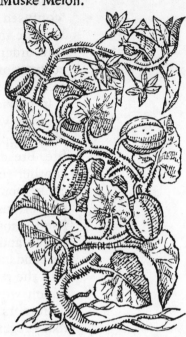

1 *Melo.*
The Muske Melon.

another. After the time of our landing many of the company digged certaine plats of ground and spred divers sortes of seeds to make triall of the ground and for certaine they were seene above the ground sprung up the fourth day after their sowing and amoungst the rest of the seeds, the Cowcumber and the Mellon were forward, we have set and sowed fourescore and one sorts of seeds, it was ten dayes before the shippes comming away, and for the most part they are all come up. Also we have Olives grow with us but no great store. Altho they have made a greate deale of Tobacco and if some would come that have skill in making it it would be very commodious both to the Merchant and to the maker of it. And for the silke worme, if any were brought over, and some skill to use them, there would be very much good done with them.

The colony established itself quickly and soon a relatively sophisticated society grew up. In the first 50 years among the trades mentioned in the records were blacksmiths, weavers, carpenters, joiners, boatwrights, tailors, shoemakers, masons, plasterers and their apprentices plus 'chirurgeons', amongst others. Acts and Regulations governing all aspects of life were passed; letters and agreements of every kind have been handed down to us.

It is extremely hard for us now to visualise what the islands must have been like: covered with cedars and palmettoes, an occasional stand of yellowwood and hackberry; the houses all built of wood with roofs thatched with palmetto. Norwood's

3

first *Survey* was done in 1618 so the portions of land were soon marked and, he commented, there was everything from 'confused Chaos, to receive a disposition, forme and order and become indeed a Plantation'.

In order to understand why particular plants were chosen for cultivation, it is useful to consider the diet of seventeenth century people and what they used to make their clothes.

In previous centuries, and until the eighteenth century, much cooking was done in a large pot hanging over an open fire in a large fireplace with meat roasting on a spit in front of the same fire. Bread ovens were separate and to one side with sometimes another fire heating them. In those ovens not only bread was cooked but pies and tarts as well. The pastry cases were known as 'coffyns' and they served the purpose of holding a meal in itself, most convenient in a day and age when there were few plates and utensils. The meat pasty and the sausage roll are descendants. A proper pasty contains meat, potato and onion. Into the pot hanging over the fire went 'pottages' or thick soups which would contain meat or fish and vegetables of all sorts, both roots and greens. The greens were often the tops of what we today regard as root vegetables only. The fast days ordered by the Church played an important role in the diet for, on a fast day, it might be that not just meat was forbidden but even fish, and therefore eggs and vegetables, or vegetables alone must suffice. Food had a sweet/sour taste achieved by adding dried fruits such as raisins, currants, sultanas and dates plus verjuice to the meat or fish in the pot. All this was seasoned with ginger, cinammon and pepper. Later clove, mace and nutmeg were also used. Verjuice came from either crab apples or grapes and provided an acid taste and fruity aroma. The 'mincepie' and 'mincemeat' are examples of this type of cookery and cassava pie is a Bermudian variation. Herbs such as hyssop, sorrel, borage, violets, mallow, betony, snakeweed and marigolds were used. The aromatic herbs were used later when savoury cooking became popular and are the ones we use now. Ginger, mustard and pepper nigra were the original hot spices. The capsicum type of pepper was a discovery of the Americas. Saffron was valued not only for its taste but for the colour it gave. It is completely inaccurate to claim that spices were used to mask the taste of food which had gone bad — they were much too precious and expensive for that. Their prime value was to enliven fast-day food and to convey the strong taste that people of those earlier centuries valued.

It so happened that the change from sweet/sour cookery to savoury cookery started to occur at the turn of the seventeenth century; and because of changes in religious views fast days became fewer in Protestant lands. In the first eighty years of the colony it appears that only twice was a fast day called for.

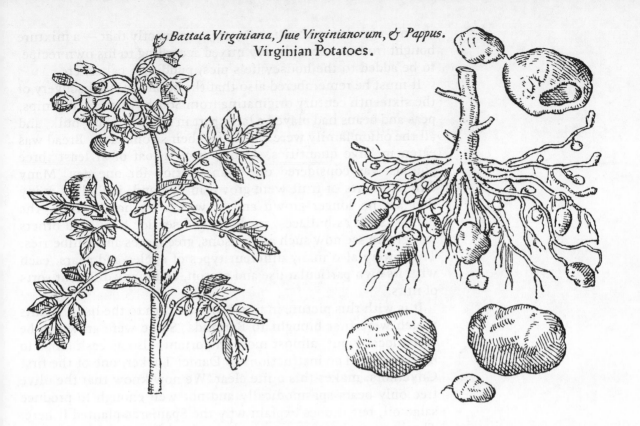

Battata Virginiana, ſiue Virginianorum, & Pappus.
Virginian Potatoes.

People's eating habits do not change quickly; it is a gradual process, and the people who first landed must have used open cooking pots from sheer necessity. Lefroy states that pumpkins, potatoes and fish became the staple diet of the people and it is perfectly comprehensible that they were all put in one pot. There is a recipe in Hugh Plat's book *Delights for Ladies*, published in England in 1600, for boiling fish with white wine, thyme, rosemary, mace, pepper, verjuice, salt and butter. There is another in a book by Robert May, dated 1660, for boiling a chine of mutton in a pot which also contained thyme, parsley, marjoram, carrots, raisins, prunes, marigolds and lemons. No doubt the sophistication of this was missing in Bermuda for a few years but the *Rich Papers* do give some clues through their requests for items. The large chimney-places were also used for hanging salted hams for smoking over wood shavings, horse litter and cedar (juniper) berries, for hanging up herbs to dry and for storing strings of sausages.

Salads were eaten too, dressed with oil and vinegar, pepper and sugar. Simple salads were all green leaves, roots and herbs but 'compound' ones contained fruit as well. A great deal of pickling, preserving and distilling was done. Hot spicy sauces and sauces similar to our ketchups were made and used for adding to recipes. 'Sugar and spice' which figure in the nursery rhyme, and also in the *Rich Papers*, was exactly that — a mixture bought from a grocer already mixed according to his own recipe, to be added to the housewife's pies, puddings, cakes, etc.

It must be remembered also that the potato was a discovery of the sixteenth century originating from South America. Parsnips, peas and beans had played a large part in diet providing bulk, and all the onion family were valued for their strong taste. Bread was eaten in large quantities. At one time a loaf of at least three pounds was considered one man's ration for one day. Many different sorts of fruit were grown in England, including many that are no longer grown and of which we hardly know the names, such as bullaces, medlars, and service trees, and others we seldom see now such as damsons, greengages and mulberries. There were also many different types of apples and pears, each with its own particular use and season, and many different sorts of nuts.

It is with this picture in mind that we turn to the list of plants which were first brought to Bermuda. Some were grown to be eaten locally but, almost more important, also as cash crops to be exported. The instructions to Daniel Tucker, one of the first Governors, makes this quite clear. We now know that the olive tree only bears spasmodically and not well enough to produce salad oil, but it does explain why the Spaniards planted it here. The beans, carrots, cassava, cucumber, figs, lemons, lettuce, limes, melons, onions, parsnips, peas, pineapples, plantains, pomegranates, potatoes (both sweet and 'Irish'), radish and sugar-cane could have been for local use but there are many references to the export of them. Grape vines were established and in the *Rich Papers* there is a request for a 'Vinnerone' to be sent (one skilled in the growing of vines). It was suggested he should come from the Canaries. Mulberries were established in the hope that a silk trade might be started. This was a particular project of King James I who disliked the cultivation of tobacco and would far rather have seen a silk trade develop. Tobacco was the largest crop, and was used as currency, but rents were paid in other commodities besides — oranges, lemons, potatoes and pepper. The people tried to dry the figs which were obviously prolific at the time, but the ants got at the fruit until a system was devised whereby the wood was dipped in tar to keep them off the drying trays. Of the spices and herbs that were grown anise had both medicinal and culinary uses and fennel, producing the same oils, was also grown. Marjoram had medicinal, culinary and dye uses, while basil, though not as hardy, had culinary and medicinal uses. Saffron was expected to be a valuable crop. It had its culinary and medicinal uses but also was a very important dye. Madder and indigo were also dye plants. Flax was grown and hemp, which was used not only for rope making but also for fabricating tough working clothes. Cedar wood was already prized, so it explains the pleasure of the discovery of it on the islands. It was known to have enduring qualities and its scent was also valued, the sawdust being thrown on fires to scent the room, particularly in times of sickness. It was also put into pot-pourris.

Those early years of the colony were difficult ones. Life must have been hard — imagine for a moment the problems of obtaining water; but the crops did grow in spite of the plague of rats. In Governor Moore's time the rats arrived on a ship and they swam from island to island. The fish ate them on the way. Dogs were trained to catch them and cats allowed to run wild in an attempt to control the plague. Somerset Island was planted with corn, the settlers hoping that they might be able to keep one island free. 'Yellow ratsbane' (probably arsenic) was sent from England by the Company. Robert Rich complained in his letters about the rats and asked for two rat-catchers and a plentiful supply of fresh ratsbane to be sent to him. The plague disappeared after about two or three years.

Robert Rich has left very good descriptions of his garden and orchard — of one acre each, fenced with fig and pomegranate, buzzing with the bees which had been sent from England. This was in 1617.

There were failures and there were problems but it was more than mere survival. In 1620 it was necessary to pass an Act to

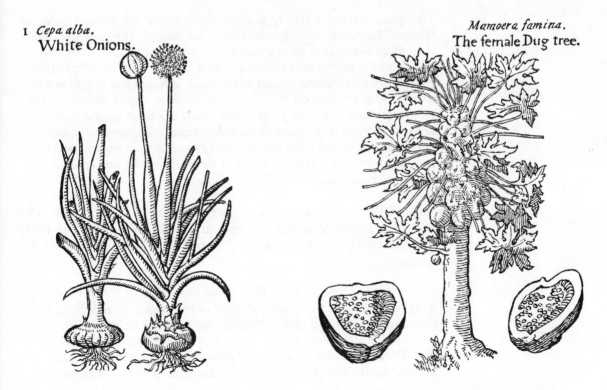

1 *Cepa alba.*
White Onions.

Mamoera famina.
The female Dug tree.

maintain sufficient fences and to forbid the felling of trees that marked boundaries. If the natural palmetto fence failed, pomegranate and fig were to be planted. People were greedy about palmettoes, the tops of which could be eaten like cabbage, so the trees had to be protected. The same year, 1620, also saw another Act insisting that turkeys must be taken in at planting time. However Captain John Smith's description of 1619–1622 confirms the prosperity. He describes a party of Spaniards who had been wrecked on Bermuda. Eventually they departed for Virginia, and Nathaniel Butler, Governor of the day, sent with them:

two great chests filled with all such kinds and sorts of fruits and plants as their islands had; as figs, pomegranates, oranges, lemons, sugar canes, plantanes, potatoes, pawpaws, cassado roots, red pepper, the prickle pear and the like.

Later a small ship came from Virginia to Bermuda bringing thanks for the presents and

much aquavitae, Oil, Sacke and Bricks they brought in exchange of more Fruits and plants, ducks, Turkies and Limestone of which she had plenty and so returned.

At this time it was also discovered that if corn was left unhusked it was protected from the weevil.

This yeare having a very faire crop, some of the Inhabitants, none of the best husbands, hastily gathered it for feare of the penaltie, threw it in great heaps into their houses unhusked, and so let it lie four or five months, which was thought would have spoiled it; where the good husbands husked it, and with much labour hung it up, where the flies did so blow on it, they increased to so many weavels, they generally complained of great losse; but those good fellowes that never cared but from hand to mouth, made great boasts that not a graine of theirs had been touched nor hurt, there being no better way to preserve it then by letting it lie in its huske and spare an infinite labour formerly had been used.

In 1639 two Spanish ships were wrecked on the reefs. The people got ashore safely on rafts and were put up in the little 'farms', two or three to a 'farm'. 'Farm' was the word used by the narrator.

Lovely orange trees, intertwined vines and other fruit trees make a delightful setting, the rooms all well planned and furnished, in every way comfortable and clean. Wild palms in green fields . . . so beautiful. Each house has its portion of land allotted and marked out. They sow tobacco, corn and potatoes and yucca for making cassava flour. The poorest is not without his patch for raising tobacco, it is the staple crop. A great abundance of potatoes and corn, the ordinary food of the working people. Potatoes are very large, I have eaten many [sweet potatoes] more than two pounds each, with good taste and flavour. There are some cattle, everyone breeds them to provide salt beef. They also raise pigs. They make a very rich and delicious fresh butter from large quantity of cow's milk. There are a good number of chicken and capons, which run about woods eating wild berries and sometimes they are given a little corn. Large flocks of turkeys. In most of the farms there are orange and lemon trees, very beautiful large fruit. Many vineyards and rose trees and countless groves of fig trees, we were able to pick the fruit, figs small and all the more delicious because not cultivated. Numerous palms and junipers make entire island a pleasant wooded retreat. There is very little water, on some farms there are wells.

The end of the seventeenth century seems to have been a time of deterioration generally. Whatever the reasons farming had by then become very unprofitable. The Bermuda Company's responsibilities were handed over to the Council of Trade and Plantations in 1684.

Governor Robinson, one of the first Royal Governors, wrote on the 11th June 1687 to England that the soil was very productive if it was manured; it was two feet deep in places although a sixth part was rocky and 'unmanurable'. However there were no poisonous 'herbs' although the wire-weed (*Sida carpinfolia* [Britton]) was bad. He commented that though previously the islands had been well wooded there were by then, 1687, few cedars left. He blamed the situation on shipbuilding and described the blasted fruit trees, withered oranges and how destructive the 'worms' had been latterly. Even in the early days of the colony there were many complaints about wind — shown for instance in the provision in leases for rents to be paid late if the crops were destroyed by hurricanes and winds. It seems that by 1687 so much shelter had been removed, which formerly had been mostly provided by the cedars, that it was not surprising that farming should have deteriorated. Part of it was carelessness on the part of the farmers — such things as packing the bad tobacco in with the good so that it all arrived rotten; part was attributable to trade tariffs and the quality of the crops. For example Virginian tobacco and West Indian sugar were so much better than Bermudian. The climate was not right for vines — later in the eighteenth century there is a description by a visitor of being given the local wine but finding it was pretty unpalatable. High humidity is known to cause the cocoons of the silk worm to rot so that might have been the reason for the lack of success in the silk trade. But more than that the Bermudians had discovered they would far rather build their sloops out of the local cedar and go a-trading in them. The cedar ships were renowned for speed and durability — they did not need caulking as often as the oak ones. All the men went — white and black, freeman and slave — leaving the old, the women and children.

Part of that same report of Govenor Robinson's dated 11th June, 1687 makes interesting reading for its description of the people of Bermuda at that time. (The spelling is Governor Robinson's, the punctuation the author's.)

The people are generally of quick growth and of pretty easie tempers but a little two affected with theire one opinions, ye which through naturall ignorance renders them not only a little uneasie to government but to themselves. The men are generally saylors, severall haveing been instructed by ould Norwood who lived here many years, they are verry hardey but of unexperienced Courage. Ye Women are likewise of a large growth and skillful in swiming and pilotting, they are comonly good huswives and verry amorous. Their Children have but little Education their parents genious together with ye place neither covetting nor affording it, they are chiefly exercised in fishing, swimming, diving, diging and ye like sciences to be artists in which they need no greate instructions their verry nature saving them boath ye charge and trouble. Ye men, women and children are all great smokers of tobacco and according to ye best estimacon we are capable of giving, expends twenty thousand pounds yearly. Ye generallity of ye People are very frugall in their apparrill, Eating, drinking and house furniture; fish, patatos and a sort of loblolly made of Indian Corne and water being theire most accustomed food and subsistance, their general drink is adams ale [water] which they receive by shedds into sisterns digged in a saft

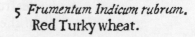

4 *Frumentum Indicum luteum.*
Yellow Turky wheat.

5 *Frumentum Indicum rubrum.*
Red Turky wheat.

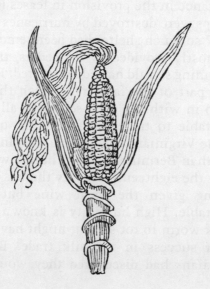

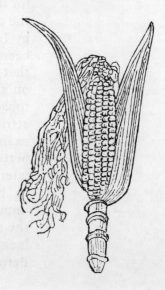

rock and plastered with tarris. Their weddings are kept most, an end kept for three days where ye young people resort early and continue danceing till Morpheus charme their weared sences. They deck [decorate] with rosemary, theire entertainment is a dram of rummy punch and a pipe of tobacco unless it is some of ye better sort whose parents adds a dinner and some bottels of wine. It hath been often observed it ye maids on their departure salutes ye fidler which he excepts for currant pay. Their Funeralls are Performed in ye Day time with little obsequies, ye Minister standing newter till ye corps be interred, who then goes to ye deceased friends with ye rest of ye company where is two or three dishes of broken bread, some rum punch and pipe of tobacco and perhaps a glass or two of wine, sundry resorting to ye Churchyard for pott hearbs.

The eighteenth century presents us with an enigma. In November 1700 Edward Randolph was writing to the Council in England:

Formerly great quantities of oranges sent yearly to England but now the orange trees blasted, the ground barren and over run with ants, they cannot raise Indian corn, it has to be imported and they now make little tobacco. Sometimes they export fish, onions and cabbages.

However the accounts of the next years provide us with an answer over the tobacco — as the duty on it was raised so profits went down; previously it had been tenants who grew it and paid their rents with it. They had been forbidden to cut the cedars. Now the owners of the land (freeholders) planted less tobacco and let the cedars grow up for shipbuilding. Consequently they started importing food. It is in these years we start hearing of plaitware (hats and baskets made of palmetto leaves). It was exported both to the West Indies and to England. There are many descriptions of the poverty of the people, except for two or three prosperous men. Governor John Hope suggested in the early 1720s that plait should be taken in payment but he also wonders how long the manufacture of plait will last as 'in sixty to seventy years it is not perceived that any plant has advanced an inch' (meaning the palmetto trees).

John Hope had arrived as Governor in March 1722 for a period of duty of six years. His *Private Letter Book* gives some interesting information about Bermuda at that time. His first letter went to Lord Carteret thanking him for giving the job of Governor to Hope. He first recounted how very difficult it had been to find Bermuda — presumably someone's navigation was not as good as it might have been.

One of most romantic like places ... very much resembles those islands upon the coast of Sweden save that the grounds that are not covered with Cedars are of a beautiful Verdure and here and there a palmeto tree growing, all the Country look like one continued Village and every house in it as white as snow.

He then describes the white people of Bermuda as having

English faces but browner complexions. Tall, lean, strong limbed ... I mean of plants there are a great many here but nobody minds them and it is not in my power to procure a few cedar berries till the season comes that I can so gather them. Formerly this place was famous for the best pineapples but now the Negroes are so multiplied and so mischievous that there's no preserving them from them.

In 1724 he wrote to Barbados

This place is in very great want of provisions of all kinds though nothing ever comes to a good market but indian corn.

In another letter to Lord Carteret in 1723 he describes the whaling that was then being carried on:

This is an admirable season for our whale fishing which I have the pleasure of every morning for three or four hours a horseback. I can seriously see them killed distinctly from the top of the hills and as they draw the boat after them along the Shoar I gallop after and seldom fail of being in at the death of the whale.

There are many mentions in his letters of the trade in 'train oyl' (whale oil) which was sent to England and also to the West Indies and Barbados in exchange for rum and sugar. He claimed in 1722 that he had killed a whale himself. Some of his letters contain shopping lists. Some items are personal such as 'a pair of spectacles for a man of about forty years of age', others are for the house and kitchen such as 'three gallons of sallad oil', 'one oiled cloth for laying upon floor under table fourteen feet long and twelve broad, locks and hinges for large cedar trunks' and finally 'and ballast with coal for my kitchen'.

By 1730 Governor Pitt is writing:

There are some small quantities of corn, onions, cabbages and oranges being produced but none for many years shipped off except onions in small quantity ... the inhabitants are decreased within these four years by about two thousand being obliged to remove because of poverty.

By 1735 there is a very slightly more cheerful picture in a report. It is very clearly spelled out that naval stores could be cultivated in Bermuda but this must in no way interfere with the trade or produce of Great Britain. The produce of the islands are named as cedar, palmetto trees and 'train oyl' — interestingly a prerequisite of the Governor. Poor John Hope had had great difficulty in selling his. The shipbuilding and plaitware is mentioned and small quantities of tobacco, pineapples, oranges, onions, potatoes and cabbages. The report also says the cedar sloops were often sold and the proceeds provided the Bermudians with what they needed. The final suggestion is that vineyards should be encouraged. Governor Pitt, writing that same year (1735) mentions the quarrying of stone which was exported but that the price of plait had fallen and from the eight to ten thousand pounds a year it used to make it had fallen so low 'that it's esteemed not worth the labour of making whereby the poorer sort of inhabitants are reduced to great extremity'. He mentions the export of not only what was listed before but live cattle, plenty of ducks, turkeys and several other sorts of poultry. In 1735 there was also an Act passed to encourage the planting of sugar-cane, ginger and cotton wool (meaning cotton). By the 1740s there were several Acts passed forbidding the export of various things as the people were in such want. In June 1743 Captain Puech had loaded 'ten fatt cattle' to be sold elsewhere but it was decided in Governor's Council that, though he should be allowed to take those, no more should be allowed.

The 1760s well illustrate the enigma referred to. A letter by Governor Bruere to the Council dated September 17th, 1765 said:

The islands will produce almost anything we may sow or plant with little trouble. It yielded potatoes, barley, coffee, lemons, oranges, onions and a little wheat and cotton. Of land held in private ownership only one tenth thus cultivated. Half of rest pasture for cattle, a few horses, other half covered with cedars. The cleared land is occupied by inhabitants in farms of fifty acres each in average, forming narrow unfenced strips on which they tie horses and cattle. Agriculture is chiefly in Devonshire, Pembroke, Paget and Warwick. Only enough provisions raised for three months of the year. Some fishing done but not as much as could have been. There is no market but their method is to kill a sheep and borrow and lend a joint when opportunity or conveniency offers. Ship carpentery gives employment, specially in St. George's. Ducks, cabbages, onions are exported. The cultivation of soil is regarded as positively degrading.
His final sally reads:
. . . without art, cultivation or agriculture.

However there is a letter from Thomas Parsons to Sir Francis Dashwood dated 3rd November, 1762. Admittedly he was applying for the job of Collector of Customs and so it can be presumed he wanted to present a favourable picture.

We raise an abundance of poultry, I suppose there are not less than 30,000 ducks shipped off in the months of May and June for the West Indies as an overplus of stock, they sell there from three pounds five shillings to ten shillings a dozen. The Turkeys that are sent from hence sell from twelve shillings and sixpence to sixteen shillings or twenty-four shillings a piece, if our vessels have no very long passages they will clear by ducks and onions not less than three hundred to three hundred and fifty pounds a trip and in the fall of the year we ship of an immense number of oranges, lemons, limes to North America. We have cows, sheep, Beeves, horses, hogs and goats.

He goes on to say how beautiful the islands are but completely untamed, no road wider than six feet although there was a law passed to make them fourteen feet. He incidentally blames the lack of roads for the lack of carriages. He mentions fortunes made in Bermuda hats but points out that there is no market. He says the food is very bad, mostly North American salt pork which leads to scurvy and therefore they are a miserable lot of people.

Seven months in the year we raise the best West Indian potatoes and pumpkins which the inhabitants give the preference to any kind of bread though we import great quantities of flower and indian corn.

Amidst all this plenty there are descriptions by other writers of emigration to East Florida at this time because of poverty and distress.

In the 1770s there were more descriptions of poverty and it was the threat of blockade during the American War of Independence that drove Colonel Henry Tucker, with his relations, to concoct the Gunpowder Steal. On January 5th, 1773 Henry Tucker wrote to St George in Virginia.

We are now in a starving condition here, not a grain of corn to be sold in the Island. A vessel from Charles Town luckily put in here, in her way to the West Indies which was a relief to the people but the extravagant price the Rice and Flour is sold at is almost as bad as the famine; the former at twenty-seven shillings per hundred weight by the cask and flour at thirty-five shillings per hundred weight prices that were never I believe known here before and I know not how the poor people do to purchase it. . . . endeavour to procure you a barrel of Oranges and Lemons to send . . . I shall send two pots of preserved oranges . . . the great scarcity of sugar prevents me sending more.

Two days previously, however, his sister Anne had managed to send two pots. Two years later Henry was still telling of the great shortage of provisions.

By 1778 the cedars had grown back for Philip Freneau was able

14

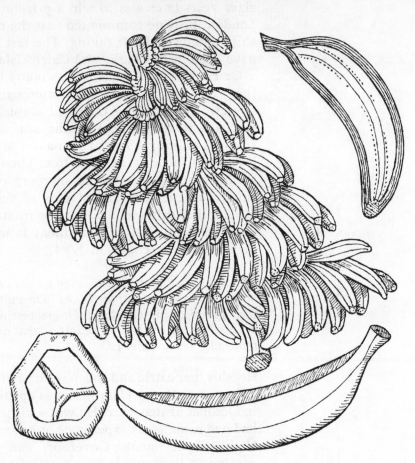

to write in May that he was amazed that so many people could be supported by so little, cedars being the only thing cultivated. The original pigs were much diminished but there was plenty of fish, and corn, flour and pork were imported. He describes the delightful shade of the cedars which protected the islands from the north-westerly winds. He said by far the greater part of the islands was covered with cedar with every now and again a cluster of orange trees giving off a delicious smell. There were fig trees and in some places plantains and bananas; however these last were not common because of the wind. He also mentions the selling of slate to the West Indies.

In 1781 Governor William Browne was appointed. He had received instructions from the King to grow cotton, but he found this extremely difficult as both the wind and salt spray were deleterious. Hedges did not provide enough protection and tall trees were not available, consequently only a small quantity could be grown. However, forty acres were planted at Tucker's Town. The cotton was woven and dyed at Ireland Island and sixty years later was to win a prize at the Great Exhibition in London. Browne commented that the natives were engrossed in shipbuilding and salt raking. The last activity would of course have been in the Turks and Caicos Islands.

Dr Francis Forbes has left us many letters about Bermuda in the 1780s. One is particularly interesting from the farming point of view. He complains the cattle are sick and covered with ticks. He tried washing them in the sea, unsuccessfully, and then suggests making a sort of sauna out of palmetto leaves, merely leaving the nose of the beast free. Then he suggests smoking the animal with a mixture of mercury ointment and brimstone smoke, or mercury and steams of sulphur. He reminded his readers that this was a poisonous mixture.

An interesting social comment is made by another Frenchman, Jean Crevecoeur, in 1784.

All land not cultivated is covered by red cedars with which they build sloops of two hundred tons. The cultivation of red cedar is their principal interest and their greatest wealth. A girl's fortune is counted by the number of cedars — that of my hostess had been two thousand, seven hundred.

He adds that cattle and sheep were pastured on the small islands.

Governor Henry Hamilton was appointed in 1788 and arrived in October of that year. He was a vigorous, observant man who had had some years experience of America both as an officer in a Highland Regiment, Governor, and prisoner of war before coming to Bermuda and he was related by marriage to Bishop Berkeley. He wrote almost immediately to John Pitt, second Earl of Chatham, about his impressions of Bermuda and a report of the survey of the Harbour being done at the time with a view to making a 'War station'. In May 1790 he wrote a lengthy note, possibly to be used for a detailed report, entitled 'of the soil and productions of Bermuda'.

The soil is either a light grayish sand and sufficiently fertile nature or a deep tenacious clay of a blood red which when opened and mixed with manure, especially sea sand or shells becomes wonderfully productive. It is easily kept in heart by the various manures which are to be had in great abundance, and from the narrowness of the land easily transported to any part — shells, seaweed, sea sand, Cedar brush trenched in or burnt — stable litter etc. is as yet little in use, owing to the injudicious method of tethering the cattle, by which the pasture is trampled down, while the poor beasts are exposed to the heats and inclemency of this Climate.

He goes on to describe the stone and its use for building; considering it to be an unhealthy material for the purpose as 'it imbibes large quantities of moisture'. He thought that the first buildings made of cedar must have been much healthier.

The cedar trees freely take root in it [the stone] *which occasions many whimsical appearances.*

He then lists six different grains, seven different pulses, nineteen different vegetables or 'roots', nineteen different fruit trees, five different grasses, nine different 'herbs and shrubs' and seven different 'forest' trees, many of which have not been mentioned by any previous writer.

Grain — *Red wheat, Barley oats, Maize or Indian corn, guinea corn, millet.*

Pulse — *Peas, beans, garavancos, Lima bean, Bonavista beans, blackeyed peas, pigeon peas.*

Roots, etc — *Carrots, cabages, Bermuda and Spanish potatoes, beets, onions, Celery, Arrowroot, Yams, Broccoli, Asparagus, Eddows, cauliflowers, spinache, salleting, cucumbers, gourds, musk and water Mellons.*

Trees — *Oranges, lemons, limes, Chadicks, guavas, apples, cherries, strawberries, peaches, pomegranates, figs, grapes, Sherries, grenadillas, olives, Mulberries — Plantains, Papaws, Bananas.*

Grasses — *Crab grass, Mellilot, Guinea grass, foxtail and clover.*

Herbs and Shrubs — *Cotton, Coffee, Indigo, Rhubarb, Sarsaparilla, Ipecacuanha, lavender, etc. Aloe, Castor Oyl Tree.*

Forest Trees — *Cedar, Palmetto, Calabash tree, Tamarind tree, Julip tree, Mangrove, locust.*

If he lists these things as growing the answer must be that many of them had been there for quite some years. The rest of his comments are worth quoting in full. The population at the time was about 14,000 people.

The richness of the soil, and the mildness of the climate have not however directed the attention of the Bermudians to a cultivation of their lands. The legislature has however held out premiums for the planting of Cedar, and sowing barley, which last has already produced this effect, that five times the quantity ever known in these Islands was sowed last Season. Fisheries are carryed on languidly though they might be rendered extensively useful — but in justice to the people the following question may reasonably be asked — Vizt. How can people launch vigorously into this or any other branch of trade which demands a considerable capital. Twenty-five acres of land is the portion of the generality of

*landholders not one in the Islands exceeds one hundred — seeing
their fortunes are not to be raised or large families fed, educated,
and put into busyness with a fund so very slender, the Inhabitants
principale turn their views Seaward, and neglect their lands to so
great a degree that almost every year famine threatens and a
considerable share of their earnings by being Carriers, and by
building ships is payd away to the Americans for Grain.*

His comments about the pasturing of cattle may come as a
surprise to Bermudians who have always pastured cattle in the
same way — as indeed did many other communities. But
conserving pasture, allowing it to renew itself, considering the
wasteful nature of cattle, was no strange idea to an educated
man. Farming, horticulture and gardening were all at a
sophisticated and successful level by the eighteenth century in
other countries and it is possible that the derogatory remarks
about Bermudians' efforts were made when the contrast with
elsewhere was noted. In 1772 John Ellis had published a book
entitled *Botanical Tracts* or *Directions for bringing over seeds to
American Colonies and use in West Indian Islands*. It is obvious
that people were very aware of the depredations of insects and
used various preparations as insecticides — sulphur, mercury,
ammonia, brimstone and tobacco. Now we must pose the
question: was it ignorance, a straight lack of the wherewithal or
idleness that prevented Bermudians from using them? Yet Dr
Forbes seemed to have the necessary provisions.

It may seem to us reading of all the produce that the
derogatory remarks were perhaps unfair, but what seemed to
annoy the seventeenth, eighteenth and nineteenth century
commentators was the failure to use the opportunities offered.
The land was fertile and productive, yet was being neglected or
ill-used. All through the years the comment recurred that
cultivation of the soil was regarded as positively degrading. This
seems to have had its beginnings in the fact that originally the
best slaves were taken on the ships, taught a trade or taken into
the houses. It was only those who were considered to be
worthless for anything else who were put to cultivating the land.
The Bermudians had also caught the planter mentality from
other places. There is a vivid description of a young white man
dawdling away the day watching an elderly black woman slowly
picking potatoes when, as the observer says, he could with the
aid of a plough have done the job in half the time himself.

In 1792 some young people called Wadsworth came to the
islands. It is a sad story. They were from New England and had
come to Bermuda as the sister had consumption, from which she
did eventually die. *The Bermuda Historical Quarterly* reprinted
the brother's letters to his father.

*Sower oranges grow wild in great abundance, limes and lemons without
number. Though the finest Irish potatoes can be raised here, none which
are not imported at five shillings to a dollar a bushel.*

He goes on to say there is so little to eat on the island that they rely on vessels in distress coming to port and selling cargoes to defray expenses. He sent for a horse and asked his father to send hay and corn for it as there was no hay, and the corn was so expensive. He mentions that hogs, poultry and butter were expensive, that there were no sheep but a little Indian meal. He says they bought chickens to fatten up, but again the feed was expensive. He then gives an account of the social life which he describes as being very gay with even the older ladies with powdered hair, flowers and feathers and coloured ribbons plus little hats and sashes. At this time St George's was full of refugees from the French Islands in the West Indies where revolution had broken out.

From the botanist's point of view the next person of note to arrive was François André Michaux. He and his father were both

François André Michaux — a reluctant visitor to St George's Island in 1806.

famous plant explorers; the father had originally been commissioned by Louis XVI to find useful plants in America for use in France. Father and son had set up plant nurseries in America and François André was returning to America from France in 1806 when the ship he was travelling on was taken as a prize by a British man-of-war. To his fury François André was held as a prisoner. The British ship *Leander* came to Bermuda from Halifax on its way to America to collect water. Michaux was allowed off the ship on parole during the eight days they were at St George's. He left a general description of Bermuda but particularly of St George's Island; and not much did he think of it. He reckoned at that time there were about four to five hundred species of plant on the island but he left a list of only twenty, most of which are the first mention of them being here. He comments on the denseness of the cedar growth and implies that the trees layered themselves with their branches. He gives forty to fifty feet as being the height of a cedar, with a diameter of a foot to fifteen inches. Obviously he did not see very old trees. He continues:

Agriculture is almost non-existent in Bermuda today, where formerly it was flourishing. This can be proved by the registers of the customs which mentioned the quantity of sugar and wine which were exported annually from the colony. The inhabitants actually employ the small number of negroes which they possess to cultivate vegetables and maize and to rear poultry. There are also a very small number of beasts and I have not seen in the island more than a dozen cows. One finds in the country proper enclosures to make better pasture but they are equally planted with juniperus. Provisions of all kinds are so rare and so dear, that the warships which come continually to Bermuda are not able to procure there potatoes or onions.

Twenty-three years later, in 1829, Harriet Suzette Lloyd arrived in Bermuda. She came to stay as a house guest for two years, and she wrote long letters to England describing practically everything of any interest. She gives the figure of fourteen thousand acres of land in Bermuda and of that she says four to five hundred were under cultivation. She reckons that the stigma attached to field work is responsible for the small amount. Miss Lloyd gives the acreage of the various crops: fifty of onions, fifty-one of arrowroot, one hundred and ninety-seven of potatoes, fifty-seven of barley and oats, one hundred and six of vegetables. Her picture of Bermuda is one of great lushness and a tremendous variety of plants, again with many this is the first mention there is of their being here at all. The cedars were thick and about forty feet high:

It forms entire groves and clothes all the vallies and hills from the water's edge to their very summit. . . . only in sheltered and more cultivated spots is it relieved by brighter and fuller foliage of other trees.

She describes large amounts of mangrove — Mangrove Bay was full of it — and refers to plantations of palmetto, aloes and cocoa. The fruits cultivated were melons, lime, sweet orange, mulberry, peach, grape, strawberry, water-lemon (which is or was the popular name for *Passiflora laurifolia*) sugar-apple and banana. There had apparently been many, many grapes cultivated at Tucker's Town; by her day it was possible to pick what one liked although they were no longer cultivated; there had also been a deterioration in the soil where formerly indian corn, tobacco, coffee and cotton had been grown. The land had become usurped by *Lantana salvifolia* (sage-bush) and the only exports were of arrowroot, cedar and onions. She gives a description of Admiralty House garden — now Tulo Valley — as having plantations of orange, plantain and palmetto with paths edged with aloes and cactus. Hoes were the tools used; a plough was only used in one place. Walsingham was overgrown with passionflower and there were ferns, aloe, poison weed (poison ivy), orange, lemon, citron, lime and olive growing plus plantations of indigo, banana and arrowroot. Tom Moore's calabash was a big tree even then and there was an avenue of 'over-arching cedars'. She saw tamarind trees in Warwick and there were avocado pear trees although they were not widely cultivated. She called them the 'alligator pear'. In Somerset there were thick fences of Spanish bayonet (yucca), cotton, tobacco and more plantations of arrowroot, bananas, sugar-cane, pepper and guinea corn (millet) and

there are many fine trees in Somerset — a Calabash with five hundred gourds.

She mentions many ornamental trees as well as the olive, almond, peach, fig, pomegranate, date and sago palm.

Governor Reid arrived in Bermuda in 1839. He earned a great deal of respect and admiration from some Bermudians. William Frith Williams wrote *An Historical and Statistical Account of the Bermudas* in 1848 which is dedicated in gratitude to Governor Reid. Williams claimed it was the first attempt to chronicle the history of the islands. Certainly it is an interesting book and, as well as political information, there is a great deal about the state of agriculture both before and after Governor Reid's arrival.

Reid arrived with instructions to upgrade the state of agriculture. Bermuda's importance to England had increased

21

after the Revolutionary War in America and it was essential that she should be able to feed herself and not be so vulnerable to blockade, especially as there was now the new garrison.

Reid met with opposition to his ideas and a certain inertia which he overcame with energy and by example. The prime example was the local attitude to ploughs. In 1789 it had been claimed the land was unsuitable for ploughs and consequently only hoes were used. By the time Reid arrived there were two ploughs but by 1843 the number had increased to fifty-four and a few years later the number had doubled again. The way Reid achieved this sort of result was first by example — he

ploughed to the very summit of the hills in the vicinity of his residence

and secondly he formed a committee of gentlemen, two from each Parish, to assist him in his agricultural projects. He then organised a ploughing match; each Parish in turn had to provide the competition land. James McGall and another man were brought out to the island to teach farming. Reid engaged in correspondence with the Horticultural Society of England about the problems of orange cultivation. There was a bad scale problem which had originated in the West Indies and in 1844, in the midst of all his efforts, there was a very bad hurricane which damaged what fruit trees there were, orange, lemon and peach.

McGall's Hill — this area is named after James McGall who came to Bermuda to teach the use of the plough. [Courtesy Department of Agriculture Library, Bermuda]

22

Orange seed was imported from the Azores and lemon seed was sent from London. Reid said he wished orange orchards might 'become something more than a luxury' and a staple product. Dwarf plantains and bananas were sent from Cayenne via Demerara to Bermuda. There was even correspondence on other uses for arrowroot, the making of paper for instance, of which there is an example amongst Governor Reid's papers. He was also concerned with the ideas of terracing and irrigation and there are drawings and descriptions of these plus the suggestion of guinea grass (*Panicum maximum*) being used for retention. Williams claims there were traces left in Southampton of old, rather inexpert terracing at that time, but he does not say where.

Governor Reid instituted the first Agricultural Show in 1843 and the list of classes were as follows: Barley, kidney beans, windsor beans, beet, buckwheat, cabbage, carrots, cassava, castor oil, celery, indian corn, guinea corn, coffee, cotton, cucumber, eddoes, flax, horse-radish, mangel-wurzel, oats, onions, green peas, peas, pot-herbs, Irish potatoes, sweet potatoes, pumpkin, turnip and wheat. The prizes offered were books on vine cultivation.

Amongst his papers are also his own notes made before a meeting of his agricultural committee; in these he suggests planting tamarisk along the North Shore, to provide shelter, and that cultivation of grapes should be encouraged.

So successful were Governor Reid's efforts that by 1844 the following crops were being grown in such quantities that it was worth making a return for the records entitled *Return of Ground Productions for 1844*. All Parishes grew all of them but the quantity varied so only the largest quantity for each Parish plus the total for the island is given here. (One bushel equals eight gallons.)

		Parish total		Island total	
Potatoes Sweet	Sandys	4,614	bushels	11,269½	bushels
" Irish	Smith's	3,705	"	13,435	"
Carrots	Smith's	158	"	590½	"
Turnips	Smith's	305	"	657	"
Barley	Southampton	71	"	138½	"
Rough Arrowroot	Hamilton	453,692	pounds	1,110,502	pounds
Onions	Sandys	200,700	"	332,735	"
Aloes	Smith's	50	"	52	"
Vegetables	Hamilton	192,230	"	296,617	"

The population of Bermuda at that date was approximately ten thousand people, half of them black and half white.

Unfortunately potato blight was noted in Bermuda in 1846. It was particularly bad on the South Shore and there are various letters describing the results in different Parishes. These were the years of the dreadful blight in Ireland.

Somewhere about this time the first Portuguese arrived in Bermuda. They were part of the emigration movement across the Atlantic but by 1847 the Legislature was offering a bounty to vessels that brought Portuguese settlers to Bermuda. The slaves had been freed for some years and, since no Bermudian seemed really to wish to farm if there was an alternative job, no doubt the Portuguese were a heaven-sent solution.

Governor Reid left Bermuda in 1846 having truly laid the foundation of future nineteenth century agriculture. It became a thriving industry. He had also imported various ornamental trees and shrubs and had had time to study the movements of hurricanes. He was an interesting, remarkable man to whom Bermuda should always be grateful.

A fitting end to this account of farming in Bermuda is the following description written by Mrs William Bluck who was born Laura Ann Cox of Orange Valley, Devonshire, for it gives us a glimpse back into the past and, in spite of all its troubles and some difficulties, it describes what a lovely place Bermuda was. It is a description of Devonshire Marsh in about 1860.

At the foot of the Loyal hill stretched the lovely marsh the favourite playground of the children and their cousins. The marsh was filled with large and beautiful cedars and it would take four, sometimes five of the children to span these trees with their little arms, stretched to touch the fingertips of the other child. These cedars made an umberguous shade, so that even on a bright summer day, it was like twilight under them. The ground under the trees was covered with high ferns, and the marshy border was fragrant with the pepper mints and grand mints. Cows roamed through the marsh, and in the evenings, they came home perfumed with the mints through which they had trodden during the day, each cow standing under her own tree, waiting to be milked. Stepping stones led through the marsh to the church and neighbours on the other side. The trees beside these stones were always full of birds and their nests, and singers [cicadas] singing in the hot air.

Gardens

Gardens have had their place in Bermuda from the very beginning of the colony. We have no contemporary pictures of seventeenth and eighteenth century gardens but we have many references to them. The problems of wind and drought have always been present but gardens played an essential part in life not just for their beauty and the pleasure they gave but for

1 Inwood	4 Verdmont	7 Greenfield	10 Shrewsbury
2 Monticello	5 Springfield	8 Bloomfield	
3 Rocky Bay	6 Old Post Office	9 Crossways	

Van der Aa map — a map of about 1720, showing Virginia as well.

growing both food and medicine. Many plants had more than one use and it is inconceivable that a seventeenth century woman would have set forth for the New World without her medicinal remedies, not to mention her seeds for food, dyes and clothing.

Fencing of one type or another was of great importance. It demarcated the ownership of land, excluded both wandering livestock and, in Bermuda, wild pigs, and also kept out the wilderness. In fact fencing and the demarcation of an area of order in a wild world appealed to the very basis of seventeenth century men's philosophy. God had created the Garden of Eden from wilderness and so they too must create order from wildness.

In Bermuda paling was used as fencing in the early days and soon after walls were built and pomegranate and figs were

Inwood, Paget — a stone fence and gate of one of the walled gardens.

Monticello, Smith's Parish — the walled garden with a view of Harrington Sound.

Rocky Bay, Devonshire — a decorative walkway of palmettoes.

Verdmont, Smith's Parish — palmettoes as decorative planting and terracing plus the remains of another stone fence.

planted as hedges. An Act of 1620 specifies the maintenance of 'sufficient fences and against felling of trees marking boundaries and where natural palmetto fence has failed plant pomegranate and fig'. The walled garden is what has survived of earlier gardens. In some cases it is a wall surmounted by a wooden fence interspersed with stone pillars and a wooden gate between pillars; in others it may just be a lovely old wall made of huge blocks of stone of varying sizes carefully fitted together and topped with flat stones.

The size of the walled garden varies. Some are quite small, standing independently near the house, some surround their house. Some are the only garden, some form part of a larger

Springfield, Somerset — another example of palmettoes used decoratively.

garden of lawns and trees. The small gardens near the houses were probably for flowers and herbs and pleasure but there were once much larger walled gardens. One was at 'Inwood' in Paget. It had a wall of about five feet high with buttresses to support it, enclosing about two acres. 'Inwood' was built about 1700 by Francis Jones, who was President of the Senate at the time. There are two small walled gardens at 'Inwood' in addition and farm land used to surround the house and its gardens.

Another large walled garden was at Mount Airey, St David's, which was just below the present lighthouse. In 1829 the description reads 'five acres of good garden land enclosed with a stone fence'; the rest of the description speaks of pasture and planting ground.

Wind has always been the great enemy of the gardener and farmer in Bermuda; therefore many of the old houses and their gardens are to be found in sheltered valleys. The houses are often built on an outcrop of rock or back into the hill-side, the garden being made in the fertile area. There were avenues leading to some houses and gardens — 'Inwood' had one and so did 'Walsingham' near Castle Harbour — but they could not assume great importance in islands where there were few carriages. The placing of large trees was more likely to be because of availability and depth of soil than any grand landscape design. Palmettoes do seem to have been used for decorative planting. They are endemic, hardy, useful, live to a great age and, when planted in groups or rows, give shade. A certain amount of terracing was done to achieve level areas and so small sets of steps from one level to another are a feature of gardens. Nature has chosen to decorate them with ferns and miniature begonias.

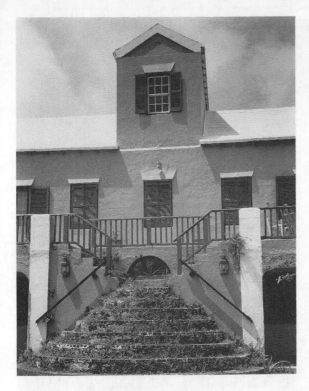

Old Post Office, Mangrove Bay — now converted to a private house the ground floor was once used for storage. The steps have been decorated by nature with ferns and begonias.

Greenfield, Somerset — more of nature's handiwork with ferns and begonias.

'Verdmont' in Smith's Parish has an example of terracing. The eastern wall of the garden is about fifteen feet in height viewed from the lower garden, a mere five feet when seen within the walls. 'Verdmont' like 'Inwood' was built about 1700, probably by John Dickinson. He was the man who sent the first collection of plants from Bermuda to Mr Petiver in London which later became part of the Sloane Herbarium. Dickinson was a busy, active man. A ship-owner and trader, he owned a shop in St George's near the Bridge House, in fact on the opposite side of the bridge that gave 'Bridge House' its name. He later became Speaker of the House of Assembly.

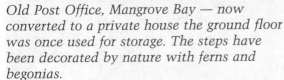

29

Springfield, Somerset — the entrance to the yard with its buttery and steps leading up to some of the outbuildings.

Terracing was also done at 'Springfield' in Somerset. The house was started in the mid eighteenth century, and the outbuildings added later. Originally the house faced northwards but, 'when the road was made', the verandah was added to the western side of the house and a new entrance made, terracing and steps built. Palmettoes provided a shady walk in from the road.

Another house started in the early eighteenth century is 'Bloomfield' in Paget. It had additions made later in the century. Its walled gardens are there for us to see, in the front and back of the house. The northern garden commands a lovely view over the harbour and sound, the southern one faces over a deep valley now containing lawns and large flowering trees. At the side of the house is another walled garden on two levels with steps between the levels.

30

All over Bermuda today one may observe the features described. Very often the houses and their gardens are not 'important' or well documented ones. The tell-tale sign of some possibly hitherto unrecorded house is a large old chimney. Below it may lie a small cottage with its little walled garden dreaming away in the sunshine. Many are difficult to photograph because of intervening roads or other houses.

The contents of those first gardens would have been herbs and vegetables. The earliest lists of plants do not specify whether they were grown as cash crops or whether they were for the islanders' own use. We do know, however, that Sir George Somers himself made a garden very soon after he landed at Gates' Bay and that he planted 'kitchen herbs', lettuce and radish, peas and onions and musk-melons. It is only knowledge of the uses to which the plants were put that makes us realise that the long list of plants which were brought in by 1616 were trade plants. Aniseed, cassava, fennel, lemons, oranges, limes, sweet potatoes, sugar-cane and pomegranates were some which were grown in fields and orchards.

Robert Rich in Bermuda wrote to his brother Nathaniel in England on 25th May, 1617:

Your garden that is payled in is fifty pole square [two hundred and seventy-five yards square] *and a well in the midst of it. Figg trees planted round about the well and vines and one* [of] *the post dyells* [a sundial?] *that I brought over with mee sett upp nere unto the well.*

Later he talks of another garden he wants to make and how he plans to fence all his ground as well as putting fig trees round yet another plot. He also mentions that other very necessary adjunct

*Bloomfield, Paget —
the northern walled
garden overlooking
the main harbour and
the sound.*

to a good garden — bees — which had been sent over by his brother. They had been put temporarily in the Governor's garden but he intended to move them at Michaelmas (September). It is possible that this is the earliest instance of bees being sent to a new colony because the ones sent to America arrived in 1638 — twenty years later. However the bees would have been sent not for their fertilising work, which was not understood at that time, but for the honey they produced.

It would appear that Robert Rich's gardens were what we would think of as vegetable gardens. It must be said though that ideas of separate flower and vegetable gardens were much less rigid in those days. There is no list of flowers as we think of them but by 1639 a shipwrecked Spaniard was able to write a most charming description of Bermuda generally, listing the contents of orchards but in particular

There are also many flowers, plants and sweet smelling herbs of the kind found in Spain; everyone has these growing in a little garden next to his home.

His mention of there being many rose trees got put in with the vineyards and groves of fig trees.

This comment by the Spaniard is the first mention of there being rose trees in Bermuda. The fact is that no seventeenth century woman would have set forth without such an important medicinal plant. All parts of the plant were used. Conserves, decoctions, ointments, syrup, honey, and rose water for cosmetic use as well as scenting rooms were all made. There are many mentions in contemporary wills and inventories of rose-stills being part of household effects. During a witchcraft trial fourteen years after the Spaniard's visit the witch was made to smell a rose. The significance of this is that anything sweet-smelling was regarded as the breath of God on earth and hence had holy and healing powers.

The types of roses would have been the damask rose (*Rosa damascena*) which was used particularly for medicinal purposes and the apothecary's rose *(Rosa gallica officinalis)*. There also may have been *Rosa alba* (the white rose) and *Rosa centifolia*. It must be remembered that it was not until the end of the eighteenth century and early nineteenth that the China roses arrived in the West and hybridisation started.

Those early years of the colony seem to have been enthusiastic ones, in spite of the dreadful plague of rats in the years 1616–19. It was said of Daniel Tucker

This Governor still spent his time in good husbandry, although some of the snarling sort here in England Whom nothing will please writ to him he was fitter to be a Gardiner than a Governor; some

time he spent in digging of a great pond but work proved altogether unprofitable and he set every one at St. George's to his task to clear grounds, fell trees, set corne, square timber, plant vines and other fruits brought out of England.

They were set to their tasks at break of day till nine in the morning and then again from three until sunset.

The people tried so many things but by the end of the seventeenth century 'the worms', 'Blasts and mildews' had discouraged them and they had turned to shipbuilding and trading in their ships. The irony was that the cutting of the cedars for various purposes had opened up the islands to those very 'blasts'.

The extra travelling which ensued meant that new and unknown plants were observed and naturally some were brought back to Bermuda. It was during the eighteenth century that

Crossways, Somerset Bridge — elegant eighteenth century gate posts.

Shrewsbury, Hog Bay Level — another example of elegant gateposts.

33

purely decorative plants were imported; at the same time useful plants were being brought back as well. Large trees such as tamarind, the West Indian locust, mahogany, calabash and Pride of India all had their uses and no doubt were intended to replace the cedars decimated by felling. The begonias, chaste tree, honeysuckle and geraniums were decorative as well as some being useful.

There are intermittent mentions of gardens because it is not possible that they could have done without them completely. In a conveyance of land in St George's some time between 1700 and 1719 appear the words '... and also all and singular yards, Gardens ...', etc. In an Inventory attached to the Will of Thomas and Parnill Wright, dated 13th August, 1713, appear the words 'In the Chamber leading into the Garden'. Governor Popple was one of the many governors who tried to encourage both agriculture and horticulture. In 1738 he had a garden. By 1759 there is a description of the 'thick cactus' overhanging the enclosing walls of the gardens of St George's; this was the prickly pear, a hopeful preventative against rats.

There are many unhappy accounts of the state of affairs in the eighteenth century: the poverty of the people, the lack of food and provisions, the hurricanes which destroyed many trees, but one really refulgent account is that of Thomas Parsons in 1762.

We have more vegetables in the winter than in the summer. Our gardens are in their prime situations from the month of September to the month of June, salary [celery] and salletting of all kinds and the choicest of garden stuff.

He lists various fruits. In the summer there were figs, musk-melons, water-melons, guavas, pomegranates and bananas and in the 'fall' orange, lemons and limes.

The best of all eighteenth century descriptions is Nathaniel Tucker's in his poem 'The Bermudian' written in 1772 while he was away from home and really meant originally to be only for family reading. He mentions many other things about Bermuda but he gives us a picture of the garden of his home which was at Port Royal. It is very much what one would expect to find elsewhere in the eighteenth century. A green lawn extending for some distance, flowering trees and shrubs, some flowers in beds, an olive tree planted on a hillock to give a view of the garden and shade to sit in.

Beneath my bending Eye, serenely neat,
Appears my ever blessed paternal seat.
Far in the front the level lawn extends,
The Zephyrs play, the nodding cypress bends,
A little Hillock stands on either side,

O'erspread with Evergreens, the Gardens Pride,
Promiscuous here appears the blushing Rose,
The Guava flourishes, the Myrtle grows,
The Earth-born Woodbines on the Surface creep,
O'er the green Beds the red Carnations peep,
Aloft their Arms triumphant Lilacks bear,
And Jessamines perfume the ambient Air.
The Whole is from an Eminence displayed,
Where the brown Olive lends his pensive Shade,
When Zephyrs there the Noontide Heat assuage,
Oft have I turn'd the meditative Page,
And calmly read the lingering Hours away,
Securely sheltered from the Blaze of Day.

This description of his adds greatly to our knowledge of what plants were growing in gardens by that date and luckily we have another description of that same garden fifty years later. In 1829 Harriet Suzette Lloyd wrote:

... approach shaded by avenue of fine tall forest trees, scattered clumps of cypress, lime, orange and magnificent West Indian Locust trees on a smooth, verdant lawn.

The Tucker family were obviously interested in plants and gardening for in letters between Henry and St George, Nathaniel's brothers, are to be found accounts of plants being sent from one to the other, in particular the Barbados flower fence (*Poinciana pulcherrima*) all carefully packed up in 'rich mould' as was the custom then. Henry was a bit anxious about it as it was 'tender' and suggested seeds might be better. He also sent seeds of the palmetto royal of which he had many. St George was in Virginia at this time and Henry in Bermuda.

Soon after this William Brown was appointed as Governor. He was related to John Winthrop and was given the appointment for his loyalty to the Crown at a difficult time in America's history. Before he arrived in 1781 he wrote asking for the garden of his house to be put in order and, although twenty-five acres surrounded Government House and was known as the Governor's Park, he requested a further purchase of land north-ward to the sea. Six years later he was still writing on this subject, this time to the Commissioners for Trade and Plantations. He asked for the land next to Government House, which had been acquired in Governor Popple's time and handed on to Mrs Bruere, wife of another Governor, be paid for — fifty-nine pounds, thirteen shillings and fourpence — so that the situation could be regularised and it could be included in the Governor's Park. He said the land was very neglected but he would clean and cultivate it. He had already built a good wall round it, with which he was very satisfied. He explained his anxiety:

*Land reserved ... no means equal to the occasions of a family as we
have no flesh market ... scantily supplied with fresh provisions.*

This merely confirms what both Thomas Parsons in 1762 and
Governor Bruere had to say in 1764 — that there was no market.
It was about 1783 when Henry Corbusier inherited it that the
garden of Orange Grove is mentioned: 'Mansion house, garden
and outbuildings'.

The tales of poverty and lack of provisions go on but nevertheless when young Daniel Wadsworth was writing to his father
in New England in 1792 for necessary provisions he did say that
he and his sister had received presents of flowers, fruit and
vegetables when they arrived. He added that the damask roses
were in full bloom.

François André Michaux, who arrived as a prisoner of war off a
Royal Navy ship in 1806, only stayed for eight days and he was
confined by parole to the island of St George's. His displeasure at
his enforced trip to Bermuda can be explained if more is known
about him. He considered himself to be a person of some
consequence, and so he was. He was a botanist of some note,
author of a book on American trees and an acquaintance of
Thomas Jefferson, at that time President of the United States
and also President of the American Philosophical Society.
Michaux had come to know Jefferson through their common
interest in plants of all kinds and by his papers being read to the
Society. Jefferson also corresponded with botanists and men of
learning in France and spent some time there as ambassador.
Michaux was very much a man of the big outside world. He
noted the small walled gardens of St George's with the prickly
pear hanging over the walls but he did not think much of
anything else he saw growing. He said he only saw pawpaw,
bananas, the most common vegetables and geraniums growing
there, plus the Pride of India trees (*Melia azerdarach*). Nevertheless, in spite of Michaux's opinions, an advertisement for the
sale of a house in St George's in the *Gazette* for December 5th,
1807, reads: 'with good garden [and] a well of excellent water'.

Harriet Suzette Lloyd provides us in 1829 with the first
detailed account of Bermudian gardens. She stayed for two years
in Bermuda and the letters she wrote were later published. She
was an intelligent and well informed observer. She writes of
plants which have not been mentioned before such as 'althea',
Hibiscus mutabilis, scarlet cordia and passion flower. Knowing
that trees and gardens take time to grow, one is tempted to think
that things may have been as she described them for some time.
She describes gardens full of fruit trees and flowering shrubs,
many roses and hedges of geraniums and vegetable gardens with
paths edged with aloe and cactus, green lawns with scattered

trees and shrubs. It was the fashion at the time she was writing to train geraniums up a trellis to form a hedge. In Bermuda she tells us they grew eight to ten feet high. The scarlet and ivy leafed pelargonium were known at this time but the dwarf bedding geranium was a plant of the 1840s. The walls are mentioned but she found them rather ugly so dismissed them, but she particularly mentioned a lack of hedges except in a few places in Somerset. As well as the avenue at the Tucker's house, 'The Grove', she mentions one of 'overarching cedars' at Walsingham. Miss Lloyd carefully made a collection of plants to be sent to England but unfortunately they got spoiled before she could send them off. The following are excerpts from her letters:

The archdeacon's residence [the house where she stayed part of the time] *is situated in Paget's; picture to yourself a very pretty cottage, which, like most of the Bermudian houses, has only one storey, and a verandah running along the whole front, covered with multiflora roses, noyau, and other creepers. It lies on a smooth, level plain, in the midst of a valley, shut in on the north-east and west, by hills covered with cedar, and sprinkled with numerous white-roofed houses, which have an exceedingly pretty effect when seen at a distance, rising from amid groves of cedar, with here and there a bright orange, or waving palmetto. The foreground is relieved by magnificent orange and shaddock trees, covered with golden fruit, and scenting the air with their rich perfume. The lawn is skirted with hedges of geranium, the pomegranate with its splendid scarlet fruit, the classic olive, oleander, coral trees, pride of India, and a variety of flowering shrubs. Towards the south, the house commands an extensive view of the Atlantic, whose blue waters wash the rocky shore which bounds the lawn. It is pleasing to watch, from the terrace, through vistas of cedars, vaulted like gothic arches, the spreading sails of a fine man-of-war proudly riding the waves. . . . with respect to the flowers there are here many whose bright tints charm the eye, but few which regale us with their perfume. There are no native roses, but several foreign varieties have been completely naturalized; such as the sweet rose, and China cluster, but the multiflora, monthly, and several others which twine round the porch and windows of the poorest hut, and bloom throughout the year, have but little scent. Many of our European flowers, when transplanted here, retain their odour only for a time. Lest, however, you should fancy that there is no redolence whatever, I must remind you of the exquisite perfume of the orange and lemon, shaddock and lime blossoms, which scent not merely the garden, but even the roadside. Then too there is the pride of India (Melia azedarach) with its fragrant lilac clusters; the delicate acacia 'bright with streaming gold', the geranium which forms entire hedges eight or ten feet high, the jessamine, the clustering woodbine and many more. Among those which please only the eye, I must mention the coraltree (Erythrina corallodendron) . . . The changeable rose (Hibiscus mutabilis) well*

*merits its name of Flos hororius; for its flowers, which are of a
delicate white in the morning, gradually assume a deeper tint till
the sun attains the meridian, when they are of a beautiful pink.*

When Governor Reid arrived in Bermuda in 1839 his first
priority was to improve and up-grade agriculture and he spent
time and energy on the project but he also had a great interest in
all plants and was responsible for many first importations to
Bermuda. The first Agricultural Show was held in 1843 during
his tenure as Governor and both *Fuschia grandiflora* and *Fuschia
globosa* were entered as well as the shell plant, geraniums and
dahlias. Fuschias and dahlias were to become popular Victorian
flowers but it is interesting that Bermuda was right there in
fashion so early. It is probable that the influence of the garrison
improved gardens locally. The Victorians were very interested in
gardens and botany. Many of the garrison had served elsewhere
and would have seen the opportunity to grow plants from other
climes here in Bermuda. What pictures and paintings we have of
the middle years of the nineteenth century also show their
fascination with palms of various kinds. It was in the 1850s that
the poinsettia, loquat and easter lily were brought to Bermuda.
Now the poinsettia and the loquat are so common it is hard to
imagine what it was like before they arrived. The other plant so
common to Bermuda, the acalypha or match-me-if-you-can was
not brought in till 1870. By 1858 we know that various of the
amaryllis family were growing here — referred to as the red lily,
the Guernsey lily and the atamasco lily. Viburnum was also
growing as were heliotrope, verbena and cannas. Some of these
were known and growing in eighteenth century America but
there is no way of knowing who brought them to Bermuda and
when. J.M. Jones edited a book *The Naturalist in Bermuda* in
1858 and his chapter entitled 'Botany' gives a good list of the
plants growing by then. Some we have met before while some
are the first mention of their being here. To end the quotations
about gardens of Bermuda the following is an evocative passage.

*Lemon which grows spontaneously everywhere, adorning the roads
and hill sides with the abundance of its golden yellow fruit. . . .
Delicious beyond description is the perfume emitted from the
expanded blossoms of these fruit-bearing trees, and more particularly
of a calm evening, after a copious fall of rain, when the sun
reappearing in subdued brightness and splendour, gilds each cedar-
crowned hill and white-washed cot with its fading beams, the
powerful scent of the citron tribe, mingled with that of the cedar, is
exhaled in such copious quantity, as forcibly to impress the
imagination with a realization of those fairy lands of ancient fable,
where gorgeous palaces inhabited by rich and happy princes, were
fanned each live-long day by balmy breezes, heavy laden with
odorous incense.*

Herbs

A definition of the word 'herb' is hard to find. So many plants, trees, shrubs and flowers are useful medicinally and so many plants had two or three uses in by-gone eras — medicinal, culinary and dyeing. The *Oxford Dictionary* definition 'Plant of which leaves, etc. are used for food, medicine, scent, flavour, etc.' is about the best that can be achieved.

Today, to be interested in herbs, to have any knowledge of them, is regarded as slightly esoteric; but the fact is that a knowledge of herbs is as old as the world itself. Primitive man used herbs and by 1000 BC Egyptians were using garlic, opium, castor oil, coriander and mint plus many other plants. Civilisation at the time of Hippocrates (after whom the doctor's oath is named) was using plants as medicines, dyes, cosmetics and scents as well as for food and magic. This was 4–300 BC. The Arab culture of the seventh and eighth centuries followed that of the Greeks and Romans who were credited with having first created the apothecary's shop as a distinct and separate establishment. Italy became the centre of civilisation in the Middle Ages and it was there that herb gardens, as we think of them, were instituted — within the monastery walls — but at the same time folk medicine existed in small homes and villages.

The first *Herbal* was written by Dioscorides during the first century AD. He was a Greek who travelled as an Army doctor. His illustrations survived and were used in later *Herbals* and were even copied in some of the medieval manuscripts. These early illustrations vary tremendously in accuracy and recognisability. This is true even of Gerard's *Herbal*, first printed in 1595 by John Gerard of London who admitted he used material from German and Italian manuscripts. In 1636 Thomas Johnson updated Gerard's *Herbal*. This is the same Thomas Johnson who displayed the first bananas to be seen in England in his apothecary's shop in London — those bananas were from Bermuda and the date was 1633.

However the seventeenth century did mark the beginning of the use of chemical drugs in medicine instead of only plants; such things as arsenic, copper sulphate, iron and sulphur. This combination persisted all through the seventeenth, eighteenth and nineteenth centuries. It is very difficult for us today to realise how recent modern medicine is.

It is also true to say that the Dark Ages, the decline of civilisation, coincided with the decline in the use of herbs and that as new light dawned so herbs started to be used once again, particularly in cooking. As stated in another chapter, the start of the seventeenth century also coincided with a change in culinary tastes and usage of herbs; from sweet/sour cooking people turned to the savoury and the uses of the aromatic herbs we know today.

The real loss of herbal knowledge occurred in the earlier years of this century, to be followed by a fairly recent revival as people, beginning to realise how chemicals were dominating their lives, conceived a wish, a longing to turn back to a more natural way of living. The modern herbalism is a part of the conservation movement. It is more sophisticated than the 'back to Nature' idea but basically it is the same revulsion against chemical additives, processed food, a packaged existence. There is a feeling of wistfulness for by-gone ages, a sense that life may have been simpler.

Interestingly, a knowledge of herbal remedies has not been lost in Bermuda. Even younger Bermudians have an interest in herbs (in the conventional sense) and they should learn from their grandparents before this knowledge is lost. The danger of such a loss is the reason a chapter on the subject is included in this book. The comparative remoteness, the lack of enduring prosperity until recent years, the old-fashioned way of life and a sturdy self-reliance, characteristic of previous generations of Bermudians, are probably the reasons why herbalism still has its place in Bermudian society today. It is only when an interest is expressed that Bermudians reciprocate with information. There is a slight feeling of diffidence that such knowledge is 'old fashioned' and therefore not of value. Nothing could be further from the truth. Many of the claims made by the ancient herbalists have now been proven by modern research, for example the use of feverfew for migraine, periwinkle against cancer, opium poppy for its morphine content, foxglove (which contains digitalis) for heart conditions, evening primrose for arthritis. This work of confirmation has really only just started but it goes on world-wide — China, Europe, England and America. The results are published in learned, specialist journals and as yet no one has collected the findings into one book. The enquirer has to keep an eye open for short articles in the daily press of different countries or articles in gardening and herbal magazines.

To some people herbal medicine seems off-beat and rather strange and many do not know what the original basis for the use of herbs was. There was, however, a proper explanation and it has a strange affinity to what is now referred to as alternative medicine or therapy. It was believed in earlier centuries that man's health depended on the balance maintained within the body between four 'humours'.

These were blood, phlegm, yellow bile and black bile or spleen. These corresponded to the four elements — air, water, fire and earth. A high proportion of blood, which was hot and moist like the air, resulted in a sanguine temperament or humour; of phlegm, which was cold and moist like the water, in a phlegmatic temperament; of yellow bile, which was hot and dry like fire, in a choleric temperament; and of black bile, which was cold and dry like the earth, in a melancholic temperament. Illness resulted when these humours became unbalanced and to restore harmony the excess humour had to be drawn off — involving the use of violent herbal emetics, purgatives and counter-irritants, as well as blood-letting, leeching and cupping. The herbs prescribed had to counter the predominant humour, so that borage and majoram, for instance would be prescribed to cheer, invigorate, warm and thus reduce a cold melancholy humour caused by an excess of black bile.

We do have some records for the first herbs brought to Bermuda. Sir George Somers planted the first garden of all in 1609 and he mentions planting 'kitchen herbs'. It is hard to know exactly what these were. In all likelihood they included parsley, mint, sage and thyme, and maybe coriander, rosemary and marigolds. However we do know from Lefroy's *Memorials* that anise, basil, cumin, fennel and sweet marjoram were all sent by the Bermuda Company to Daniel Tucker, the Governor, in 1616. They were meant to be cash crops as well as being used by the local population. What we also know is that other herbs were brought in although we have no dates of importation for them, because we see them now as 'escapes'. In other words they are growing wild all around us today — alexanders, castor oil, mint, mullein, parsley, rosemary, honeysuckle, plantain, dandelion, chicory, 'Father John', tansy, allspice, wormwood and aloe. This list may surprise the reader but it cannot be emphasised enough that many plants had not only one use but sometimes two or three — culinary, medicinal and maybe as a dye as well.

Two other points need to be considered. One is that on consultation with *Herbals* written in other countries the same remedies for the same complaints are recommended as are used here. To put it another way, the knowledge and folklore carried here to Bermuda has been handed down from one generation to another. The second point is that where a known remedy for an illness was not grown here, or did not succeed and flourish, an alternative was found amongst local plants or ones imported from the West Indies or the Americas.

To illustrate the first point, elsewhere dandelion was considered valuable as a salad ingredient, being a digestive and diuretic, and its roots were dried and used as a substitute for coffee. Here in Bermuda it was also used for coffee and considered to be good for anaemia, jaundice and improving the appetite.

Elderberries were a purgative; the bark and leaves are so strong that they are poisonous but the milder uses as an infusion cured bruises and eczema and a syrup of the berries was used for sore throats. In Bermuda elderberry was recommended for constipation and as a general tonic.

Fennel was sent to Bermuda by the Company in 1616 and taken to America at very much the same time. For many hundreds of years it has been considered to have an affinity with fish and the seeds have been eaten as a digestive. It also has been valued as an eye herb for as long. In Bermuda it was noted as an eye-wash and was said to be good for the kidneys. One extra quality cannot fail to be noted. William Coles, a seventeenth century English gardener, wrote that fennel was much used 'for those that are grown fat, to abate their unwieldiness and cause them to grow more gaunt and lank'.

Mint has always been considered to have an affinity with duck and one is tempted to think that as so many ducks were reared here in the earlier centuries it must have been imported to go with roast duck. It was certainly considered to be a digestive and sure enough in Bermuda it is recorded as being good for indigestion and constipation.

Nasturtiums were thought to have a tonic, cleansing effect and more recently have been proved to be full of minerals and vitamin C. In Bermuda they were used as a blood tonic.

Nettles were also considered to have tonic qualities, and to be good for anaemia, retention of urine, indigestion, skin diseases and rheumatism. In Bermuda the list is longer, albeit similar: anaemia, arthritis, diabetes, eczema, piles, hairgrowth, hypertension, nose bleeds and jaundice. They were also steeped in boiling water and when cooled the results used to bathe measles patients. Measles was a dreaded disease in Bermuda.

Onions, the much loved vegetable of medieval man, were also considered to be a blood cleanser and antiseptic and in certain parts of England onion soup was used for colds. In Bermuda onion and thyme together were considered good for asthma and pneumonia, for gastric upsets and hookworm. But the old St David's remedy of a roasted onion cut up in small pieces and put down the ear for earache has its counterpart in the old English use in exactly the same way, or alternatively it was used as a poultice.

Plantain, here in Bermuda known as 'rhubark', 'rhubarb' and 'cat's cradle' (the last its old English name together with 'ribwort') is another example of folklore passed from generation to generation. In England in earlier centuries it was used against insect bites and wounds and a tea used for fevers, diarrhoea and for bladder and kidney complaints. Here in Bermuda it was and is used for cuts, sprains, bruises, poultices and against hypertension.

Rosemary was traditionally used in different lands at weddings and funerals 'for decking' for hundreds of years and sure enough it was used in the same way in seventeenth and eighteenth century Bermuda. It was considered to be antiseptic and a digestive and its oil good for aches and pains, for hair preparations and cosmetics. In Bermuda the uses are so similar — for baths, to encourage hair growth, as a hair rinse and for headaches.

Thyme has always been a valuable cooking herb having both preserving qualities and a good flavour. It was valued for its antiseptic qualities as a gargle, for coughs, colds and flu. As previously noted, it was used in conjunction with onions for similar complaints locally.

Tansy is another herb with similar uses. It was used a great deal in cooking, particularly baking. It was considered to have tonic qualities, to be good for rheumatism in the form of a poultice, and to drive away fleas. Modern knowledge declares it unsuitable to be taken internally. However, in Bermuda it was and is declared to be good for the appetite and for rheumatism and to relieve stomach pains.

Let us now examine the local alternatives for complaints — not necessarily all herbal.

Alexanders were taken to North America in the sixteenth century. They had always been considered to have an affinity with fish and they were a common vegetable for fasting days. In Bermuda they came to be fed to cattle but also, together with ginger, they were made into coughdrops.

Allspice was used for 'cooling the system' by making a tea out of the leaves that were turning brown rather than the green ones.

Aloe, brought to Bermuda some time during the eighteenth century, has a long list of medicinal uses. It was, at one time, an important industry. L.H. Smith quotes from an old (undated) newspaper cutting:

First or purest kind called Succotine. Thrown on the fire it melts like wax and is so light as to swim on water. The manner of preparing it to be used medicinally is to cut leaves, collect juice, place in the sun till it becomes the proper consistency. It is also extremely bitter and purgative and applied externally prevents putrefaction and gangrene. It was an unfailing remedy for dysentery.

The juice in milk combines two properties of an anodyne and an aperient.

The canal at Wistowe, The Flatts, was cut so that a mill could be worked for the extraction of aloe juice, which was exported to America during the war of 1812 for medicinal purposes. Five acres of land at Devil's Hole was planted for the purpose at this time. It was considered a strengthener for nerves, a poultice for sores and sixty drops of juice would cure a cold. Because of the mixture of alkali and oil it formed a good lather and was used for scrubbing floors and referred to as 'bamboo'. Together with sand it made boards very white. Fibres of the plant were used for fishing lines and cordage, the softer ones being used for silk grass to sew palmetto plait. Finally it made a good spring tonic for both people and chickens, slices being put in the latter's water.

The modern usage for aloe is for burns but in old Bermuda cutting the head out of a young banana tree and applying the juicy part direct to the burn was also thought to effect a cure.

The castor oil plant was found here by the first people to arrive. It is a plant that has been used for thousands of years. It was considered in Bermuda to provide a good spring tonic, could be used against rheumatism and the leaves could be chewed against toothache.

Cedar — or juniper, which is what the local cedar is — was a prized tree in Europe before the first people arrived in Bermuda. Its berries were used in cooking pork and fish. A tea could be made to aid the digestion and it was considered to be a good fumigant in times of illness. Cedar berry syrup was one of the cough medicines in old Bermuda. Coughs must have been common for there are several remedies. The nicest was rosemary and molasses boiled together, the nastiest shark oil, aloe and honey, also boiled together. Flopper leaves (*Bryophyllum pinnatum*) boiled with honey and lemon were another. Cedar dust was put on the navel of newborn babies as a healing and drying agent.

Fig juice was considered to be good for constipation but a roasted fig, as hot as bearable, put in an aching ear which had been rubbed for a quarter of an hour first, followed by blowing tobacco smoke strongly into the ear, was another old Bermuda remedy.

Lemons had a medicinal use against headaches when boiled with rosemary leaves; the juice was a good hair rinse and made the hair shiny.

Lemon grass is used for tea locally but it is said to be good for colds and sore throats made like a lemonade.

Mulberry leaves together with nettles made into a tea were considered to be good for diabetes and hypertension.

A very popular local plant is 'Father John'. A tea should be made of its flowers, which turns red and it is considered to be a good tonic.

The local sage-bush (*Lantana*) which is a different species of plant from that called sage (*Salvia*) elsewhere, has nevertheless been put to similar uses. Sage or *Salvia officinalis* was used in England and elsewhere as a herb for fatty foods such as pork and duck but it was also used as a gargle, mouthwash, in toothpowders and for rubbing the teeth and gums. Here the sage-bush (*Lantana*) is used for freshening the breath, as a substitute toothbrush and a gargle. Some similarity in the leaves must have prompted this similar use although one type of leaf is much smaller than the other.

Pomegranates had various other uses such as dyeing and curing leather but it was found that boiling the bark to make a tea eased labour pains in childbirth.

Pawpaw juice was dripped round the circle of ringworm: the seeds were said to be good for constipation. Boiled green pawpaw was good for hypertension and liver trouble and the water it was boiled in was good for keeping blood sugar down.

One of the most interesting remedies is for blood poisoning: cut a spider lily (*Hymenocallis declinata*) root in two, heat and apply to affected parts for several hours. For mackerel poisoning eat raw sweet potatoes as quickly as possible and drink plenty of milk. Raw Irish potatoes were recommended against scurvy. There was one remedy that must have been infallible for cassava poisoning — give the patient whale oil and soap suds which will bring on a vomit. A poultice of crushed wireweed was applied to boils. Both periwinkle and wormwood tea were considered good for diabetics and periwinkle was also good for circulation, internal bleeding and 'nervousness'.

Another infallible remedy, for tetanus, must not be lost to posterity. Get as many live cockroaches as possible, crush and make a poultice, apply to the patient's back. This is purported to break the spasms. An invaluable remedy for typhoid was to cut a live pigeon down the back and apply it to the patient's feet; it would break the fever.

Many of these remedies I found in an article written by Mrs Vaughan Pugh for the *Bermuda Historical Quarterly* in 1957. The rest are listed below as they should not be lost and were at one time used frequently by the St David Islanders.

For a cough Take poppy flowers or common marigold flowers, put in a bottle, add sugar. Hang in the sun for several days to melt. Take a spoonful several times a day.

For whooping cough Slice an onion in a plate, sprinkle with brown sugar. Put in the sun to melt. Take a spoonful of juice every hour.

For hoarseness Beat egg white slightly. Squeeze a lemon in it; sweeten. Take a teaspoonful every hour.

For croup Rub chest thoroughly with goose fat and stay indoors.

For a sore throat Cut a slice of salt pork. Simmer a few minutes in vinegar. Apply to throat as hot as possible.

For mumps Make a poultice of hot ashes and apply to throat.

For toothache Cut a piece of aloe about two inches long; heat and lay on gum next to tooth. Apply castor oil tree leaves; they reduce inflammation.

For poor appetite Boil hoarhound or wild mint; sweeten and take in small quantities.

For a sprained wrist Soak in vinegar; bind tightly and keep bandage on several days.

For rheumatism Take several leaves of the castor oil tree — red stems are better. Crush and apply to affected parts.

For cuts When children got cut and bleeding continued, parents took soot from the back of the fireplace and applied it to the wound. For a festering cut apply green mould.

For sunstroke Dash water in the face; apply ice cloth or cold water. Tea or coffee may be taken soon after.

For a carbuncle Make a plaster of common soap and brown sugar.

For chilblains The smoke from a green cedar brush was a very effective cure.

For baby teething Crush raisins and put in a bag for baby to suck.

For diarrhoea Make arrowroot as a corn starch pudding, rather thin. Take often.

For a caked breast Bake large potatoes; put two or more in a woollen stocking. Crush them and apply to breast, as hot as can be borne; repeat constantly until relieved.

For styes Rub with a gold ring — wedding ring preferred.

For warts Rub on a dead body.

For boils Take skin of a boiled egg; peel it carefully; wet and apply to boil.

To stop bleeding A handful of flour bound on the cut.

For sores Crush geranium leaves; mix with fat and apply to sore.

For constipation Mix salt water and molasses and take often.

For shingles Drink salt water for a week; then bathe in sea water.

For an ingrowing nail Pour boiling water on ribwort and bathe the affected nail.

To restore from stroke of lightning Shower with cold water for two hours. If the patient does not show signs of life put salt in the water and continue to shower an hour longer. (This remedy was used 130 years ago.)

For convulsions in children Scrape tiger lily root freshly dug and apply to soles of children's feet.

Apoplexy Put a handful of salt in a pint of cold water. If possible pour this down the patient's throat. If the fit comes directly after a meal, rub the feet and hands. And let two strong men carry the patient backwards and forwards about the room.

For rash Boil mallow leaves and fat together to form an ointment and apply.

For inflamed eyes Bathe often in salt water.

For high temperature Boil leaves of wild plantain; add a little sugar and lemon and drink. Chop cochineal cactus; steep in water and drink.

For asthma Swallow live cockroaches. Their struggles with their legs break the web. Take live hog lice, twelve at a time; take a dozen a day for six days.

For worms The milk from a green pawpaw on a lump of sugar. Take before breakfast for three days.

For a delicate child Dip child in fresh sperm whale oil.

For poison ivy Bathe in warm milk with a little salt. Alternatively bathe in the sea as soon as possible.

For boils Make poultice of crushed wireweed and apply.

There is another aspect of the use of plants that ought to be considered — those useful for dyeing. Once again some of them may come as a surprise to the reader. There are no records of dyeing ever taking place here in Bermuda and it would seem from all records so far examined that most cloth and clothes were imported either ready for use or ready made. However in the early days of the colony hemp, cotton and flax were grown and weavers were listed amongst the known tradesmen. Madder and indigo were grown, both dye plants, and saffron was also tried. A list appears below of plants that grow here and do produce dye.

The other thing to be considered is which mordants were available. A mordant is an essential part of dyeing for it is the fixative for the dye and different mordants will provide different shades of a colour. The subject to be dyed, be it cotton, wool or silk, is first prepared with the mordant and then put into the dye pot which has the prepared leaves or blossoms in it. Some mordants would have been provided by using a cooking vessel made of that metal, such as tin, copper or iron. Alum is a by-product of burning wood, and so is charcoal. Alum and charcoal would have been found in the lime kilns that were necessary for building purposes to supply a cement-like product and lime washes for roofs and painting. Salt and cedar ash were obviously available and so of course was urine (ammonia). Tannic acid was also available from olivewood, buttonwood, also from pomegranate. It was obtained from the bark and would have been used for leather. Finally rainwater is a very desirable component in the dyeing process.

Bedstraw	Reddish colours, and yellow with different mordants and heat.
Brazilwood	Red.
Carrot tops	Yellow, orange, khaki, dull brown and various shades of green depending on the mordant used.
Cedar	Berries dull yellow, alum as mordant — brown or khaki.
Coreopsis	Very good red.
Coffee	Beige, coffee, also gold browns, dark yellow, and donkey grey using iron as a mordant.
Dandelion	Magenta from the roots.
Elder	Blue and lavender.
Golden Rod	Rich yellow and gold, burnt orange and brown; greens using iron as a mordant.
Hibiscus	Different colours with different mordants.
Indigo	Blues and purples.
Lichens	Browns.
Logwood	Purples, grey to black, red with different mordants.
'Old Man's beard' (*Usnea*)	Clear gold, rich red brown.
Madder	Red, orangey red, garnet, deep dark red, according to mordant.
Marigold	Yellow and gold from leaves, dark orange from the dead heads. Khaki using iron.
Magnolia	Grey.
Narcissus	Yellow.
Onions	Yellow.
Parsley	Greeny-yellows or clear greens, light brown using iron.
Prickly pear	Purple or scarlet, pink and salmon with different mordants.
Pomegranate	Yellow, brown and violet with different mordants.
Pride of India	Khaki.
Poinsettia	Red and lavender.
Rue	Red.
Sophora microphylla	Primrose yellow using the flowers, orange to tan using the seeds (alum as a mordant).
Tansy	Root — green. Leaves — yellow.
Tomato vines	Pasty and pale.

To have a knowledge of the plants growing around us adds another dimension to life and to know what varied uses to which some of them may be put should make us grateful for the wonderful and remarkable world we live in.

Index of plants
in Bermuda

Agave americana	Century plant.
ALEXANDERS *Smyrnium* *olusatrum*	These were introduced to Britain by the Romans. Once they were eaten a great deal particularly with fish. They were used as a salad herb as well as being cooked and candied. There is no date of their importation to Bermuda but they used to be fed to cattle. They grow wild or are self-sown in gardens.
ALLAMANDA sp.	Linnaeus gave this species its name but there is no importation date for Bermuda although it is mentioned by Lefroy, Britton and L.H. Smith.
Allium sp.	Onion
ALLSPICE *Pimenta dioica* *(officinalis)*	A native of the West Indies there is no indication as to when it came to Bermuda. However the wood was used for fishpots and the medicinal use is to make a tea for 'cooling the system' out of the leaves that are turning brown.
ALMOND West Indian *Terminalia catappa*	The first mention of this tree is by Suzette Lloyd in 1829 and as no other almond tree grows in Bermuda one may presume that this is what she meant.
Alpinia zerumbet	Shell plant
ALOE sp.	There are several types growing here. Governor Henry Hamilton gives us the first definite mention of it in 1790. In 1796 George Tucker recorded that it was used as a substitute for hops in

breweries. He said the crop was tried but the price had fallen by the time it reached London. However L.H. Smith recounts that the canal at Wistowe, 'The Flatts', was cut so that a mill could be worked for the extraction of juice which was exported to America during the war of 1812 for medicinal purposes. Certainly Suzette Lloyd makes several references to it in 1829. She said there were plantations of it and at Admiralty House gardens the paths were edged with aloe and cactus. It was also to be found at Walsingham. Smith's Parish was the largest producer and by 1844 it was recorded that 50 bushels came from there alone. It had several medicinal uses. Boiled with molasses it was a cough remedy, but shark oil, aloe and honey also was a cough remedy. A slice put in cold water and drunk helped with colds and inflammation and in the same way it was given to chickens as a tonic. It was supposed to be an unfailing remedy for dysentery and was used for poultices.

ALTHEA

In 1829 Suzette Lloyd just gives the one word 'althea'. This might mean what we mean today and call the rose of Sharon — *Hibiscus syriacus*, or it might mean *Hibiscus rosa-sinensis* or it even might mean a hollyhock which bears the Latin name *Alcea* today.

Anagellis arvensis   Scarlet pimpernel

Ananas comosus   Pineapple

Angel's trumpet   *Brugmansia*

Anona squamosa   Sugar apple

ANISE
Pimpinella anisum

Daniel Tucker records its importation in 1616. It contains very much the same oils as fennel but in Bermuda it is not as hardy as fennel has proved to be. In eighteenth century America each settler to Virginia had, by law, to bring six seeds and plant them. It was used in both savoury and sweet dishes, liqueurs and sweet butter. According to Gerard it was used for 'yeoxing and hicket' (hiccups!) and for 'quinzy, being gargled with honey, vinegar and a little hyssop gently boiled together'.

Apium graveolens   Celery

APPLES
Malus sp.

They were amongst the many trees planted at the beginning of the colony, according to Norwood, and Governor Hamilton saw them growing in 1790.

APRICOT *Prunus* sp.	The only mention of this fruit is in the *Rich Papers* in a letter dated 22nd February, 1617 in which Robert mourns the loss of the trees Nathaniel sent to him, saying it was the fault of the packers and next time they should be packed in a barrel half full of earth.
Arachis hypogea	Groundnut
ARROWROOT *Maranta arundinacea*	It is thought that arrowroot was brought to Bermuda some time during the eighteenth century. Certainly Governor Hamilton saw it in 1790. Suzette Lloyd mentions plantations of it at Walsingham and in Somerset. She says it was exported and that fifty-one acres were devoted to its cultivation. In 1843 there was a raging fever epidemic and Lord Mark Kerr wrote on Sunday 27th August: 'I leave my bed, take quinine, chicken broth and famous Bermuda arrowroot.' By 1844 Hamilton Parish alone produced 453,692 lbs and the whole island 1,110,502 lbs which were being exported. This was still one of the principal exports in 1868–9.
ARTICHOKE *Cynara scolymus*	Captain John Smith in his account of the island of 1623 mentions that there were plenty of 'English Artichokes' growing amongst many other crops. These would have been our globe artichoke for the Jerusalem artichoke was discovered in America and was a fairly new vegetable at that time. 'Potatoes of Canada' they were called.
Artocarpus altilis	Breadfruit
Asparagus officinalis	Another of Governor Hamilton's list of plants seen in 1790 but the only mention we have.
AVOCADO *Persea persea*	The first mention of this tree in Bermuda is by Suzette Lloyd in 1829. She said it was 'not widely cultivated' but there were trees at Walsingham. The other name used until recently was alligator pear. It was certainly known about in the eighteenth century for John Ellis in his *Botanical Tracts* of 1772, which were a collection of papers giving directions for bringing over seeds from and to the American Colonies and West Indian Islands, suggests that if the pulp were squeezed out of the fruit and the result allowed to dry it travelled safely. The other way of transport was to enclose the seeds in wax.
Avena sativa	Oats
Avicennia nitida	Black mangrove

BALSAM OF PERU
Myroxylon pereirae
Toluifera peruifera

[Britton] According to L.H. Smith, Governor Reid was responsible for importing this tree in 1845.

BANANAS
Musa sp.

Plantains are recorded as having been brought to Bermuda in 1616 but bananas must have been brought at the same time, or soon after, for the very first bananas ever to be displayed in London were shown in Thomas Johnson's shop in 1633 and those were Bermuda bananas. Thomas Johnson revised and added to John Gerard's famous *Herbal*. By 1762 Thomas Parsons was listing them as one of the summer fruits. However, Philip Freneau writing in 1778 remarked that because of the wind they were not that common. Governor Hamilton saw them in 1790 and F.A. Michaux saw them in the little walled gardens of St George's in 1806. Suzette Lloyd saw quite a lot including plantations at Walsingham and in Somerset in 1829. In 1845 Governor Reid imported *Musa sapientum* and *Musa paradisaica* and by 1868–9 they were regarded as one of the principal productions. The leaves had an extra use — for stuffing mattresses — and the old Bermuda remedy for burns was to cut out the head of a young tree and apply the juice direct to the burn.

Baptisia tinctoria

Wild indigo

BARBADOS FLOWER FENCE
Caesalpinia pulcherrima,
Poinciana pulcherrima,
Barbados Pride

Said to be named after the Italian botanist Caesalpinus 1519–1603. The first mention of this plant is by the Tucker brothers Henry and St George in 1772. Henry sent a box of plants to St George in Virginia, packed carefully in good mould. He was a bit anxious about them and suggested seeds might be better. Suzette Lloyd mentions it again in 1829. It was used as hedging material in Barbados, much as pomegranate was used in Bermuda.

BARLEY
Hordeum sp.

Governor Bruere comments in 1765 '. . . will produce almost anything we may sow or plant with little trouble . . . yielded . . . barley.' Governor Hamilton lists this amongst his *Grains* in 1790. Moreover, he says in an effort to overcome the perennial hunger of the people, 'The legislature has held out premiums for

. . . [the] sowing [of] barley, which last has already produced this effect, that five times the quantity ever known in these Islands was sowed last Season'. Suzette Lloyd in 1829 says fifty-seven acres were devoted to growing it. By 1844 Southampton produced 71 bushels and the whole island 138 bushels.

BASIL
Ocimum basilicum

Daniel Tucker gives the first mention of this in 1616. A herb that grows well here but not liking the wind. A culinary herb particularly with tomato. Gerard has this to say: 'Good for the heart and the head. Seed cureth infirmities of the heart, taketh away sorrowfulness which cometh of melancholy and maketh a man merrie and glad. Juice cleanses the dimness of the eye [conjunctivitis?] and good for snake bite.'

BAY GRAPE
Coccoloba uvifera

Both L.H. Smith and Britton consider this to be a native. It must have come on wind and tide for there is no reference to it in the earliest accounts. Suzette Lloyd has a reference to 'mangrove grape tree' and it is this. The large tree at Harmony Hall is supposed to have been planted in 1820.

BEAN
Phaseolus sp.

Sylvester Jourdan's account of 1612 mentions planting beans but with no indication of what sort. Sixteenth and seventeenth century peoples' diet contained many a bean and Governor Hamilton gives, in 1790, 'beans, Lima beans, Bonavista beans . . .'

BEDSTRAW
Galium bermudense

This is an endemic. It was one of the plants in John Dickinson's collection of 1699 sent to Mr Petiver and now in the Sloane Herbarium. It was used as stuffing for mattresses here according to Mrs Vaughan Pugh. Elsewhere bedstraw was used as rennet but also as a dye for wool. It will give reddish colours but with a different mordant and heat will provide yellow dye.

BEET
Beta vulgaris

One of the first vegetables to be planted here in 1610. It was still growing in 1790 according to Governor Hamilton and it also appeared as part of Governor Reid's list in 1843.

BEGGAR TICKS,
White
Bidens pilosa

Shepherd's needle. A widespread weed here. In the Bahamas when steeped it is used against prickly heat and for cooling the blood. It is also a dye plant, giving yellow and orange.

BEGONIA sp.

According to the *Bermuda Garden* it was introduced to Kew about 1777 and it may have been here as long. It has now naturalised and is to be found on steps and cuts in the rock.

BELL-APPLE
American

One of the trees that Suzette Lloyd mentions in 1829. It is another name for *Passiflora laurifolia* or water lemon.

BERMUDIANA *Sisyrinchium* *bermudiana*	This is an endemic and really should be considered the national flower. In 1669 Governor Sir John Heydon made an Order to pull up the 'lillies'. In earlier centuries all iris had been called lilies. The *Sisyrinchium* is of the iris family so it is considered that the Order was against the *Bermudiana*. Suzette Lloyd mentions them as growing everywhere in 1829.
Bottle gourd *Lagenaria siceraria*	
Brassica oleracea	Broccoli, cabbage, cauliflower, kohlrabi
Brassica rapa	Turnip
BRAZILWOOD *Caesalpinia echinata*	In 1658 amongst a list of things being sent to England appears the item '3,840 sticks of Brazelletta wood'. In 1723 Governor John Hope mentions that 'Brasiletto' was a product of Bermuda. It was useful as a dye plant.
BREADFRUIT *Artocarpus altilis*	Governor Reid introduced this tree in 1846. Britton mentions it as having been tried at various times but as it is a native of Polynesia the conditions are no doubt not correct.
BROCCOLI *Brassica oleracea*	Grows well in Bermuda today. Governor Hamilton gives us the first mention of it in 1790.
BRUGMANSIA Angel's trumpet *Datura suaveolens*	Another introduction of Governor Reid's in 1843.
BUTTONWOOD *Conocarpus erecta*	Mentioned by the very earliest settlers, it is said it was used for tanning leather. Certainly tanners and shoemakers are mentioned in those early years. In 1734 Revd Clerk listed it as one of his plants according to Dr Fothergill.
Byrophyllum *pinnatum*	Floppers — Life plant

| CABBAGE | There are frequent references to the export of cabbages, together with other 'productions' during the eighteenth century, although more were exported at the beginning of the century than by mid-century. However we have no date for their original importation. In 1779 there was a request for a garden for the troops to grow cabbage and Governor Hamilton mentions them in 1790. |
| *Brassica oleracea* | |

CACTUS sp.

During the seventeenth century the Turk's cap cactus — *Melocactus communis* was brought in from the Turks islands. In 1829 Suzette Lloyd was writing: 'Admiralty House garden paths were edged with aloes and cactus' but does not specify the type.

Cactus opuntia   Prickly pear

*Caesalpinia
 pulcherrima*   Barbados flower fence

Caesalpinia echinata   Brazilwood

Cajanus cajan   Pigeon pea

CALABASH
Crescentia cujete

In 1763 there was a *Paper* read to the Muséum d'Histoire Naturelle in Paris about this new species recently discovered. By 1790 Governor Hamilton referred to calabash trees here. Certainly by 1829 Suzette Lloyd says that Tom Moore's tree at Walsingham was a big tree and that there was a tree in Somerset that had five hundred gourds. These gourds were used as boat bailers and for other similar purposes. Many of the gourds came from the tree at Orange Grove, Smith's.

Calendula officinalis   Pot marigold

Cannabis sativa   Hemp

CAPE WEED
Phyla nodiflora

F.A. Michaux mentions a cape weed as being one plant he saw and in 1845 Governor Reid mentions seeds being sent to Jamaica and that the plant was introduced to Bermuda from Cape François.

Capsicum baccatum   Bird pepper

Carica papaya   Pawpaw

CARROTS *Daucus carota*	One of the first vegetables to be planted here in 1610, and still here in 1790 according to Governor Hamilton. By 1844 Smith's Parish alone produced 158 bushels, the whole island 590 bushels.
CASSAVA *Manihot esculente*	Captain John Smith is the first to mention this in 1623. A present of two great chests of fruit and vegetables were sent to Virginia and amongst them were 'Cassado' roots. By 1639 a shipwrecked Spaniard could write that in each little portion of land attached to each house amongst other things were 'yucca for making cassava flour'. By 1829 it was still growing in Somerset. The old Bermuda remedy for cassava poisoning was to give the patient whale oil and soap suds to induce a vomit. Successful, I am sure.
Cassia fistula	Golden Shower
Cassine laneana	Olivewood bark
CASTOR OIL PLANT *Ricinus communis* *Palma Christi*	Used by man for thousands of years, its first mention here is by Captain John Smith in 1623 and it was seen by Governor Hamilton in 1790. Suzette Lloyd called it *Palma Christi* in 1829. Its use in old Bermuda was against rheumatism and the leaves were chewed against toothache.
CAULIFLOWER *Brassica oleracea*	Grows very well in Bermuda today but the first reference we have is by Governor Hamilton in 1790.
CEDAR *Juniperus* *bermudiana*	An endemic. Cedar was already a much prized wood when the colony was founded both for its enduring qualities for building of houses and ships and its medicinal properties. No time was lost in making use of the local cedar, so much so that within a dozen years the Bermuda Company was enacting Orders to protect it. Attempts were made to stop the export although chests were made to convey the citrus and casks for potatoes partly in order to evade the laws. In 1655 3,000 lbs of tobacco were exported in cedar chests made of boards 'an inch and a quarter sawn', and three years later a small cedar desk was sent to England. Great destruction went on in the clearing of land and great waste took place. By 1687 Governor Robinson complained there were few cedars left and blamed shipbuilding. In 1732 timber was being brought from the Bahamas. However the cedars grew back and by 1778 Smith's Island was covered and Philip Freneau said they were the only thing cultivated (not quite true). A bride's fortune was counted in cedars. Every visitor to the islands has remarked on the cedars, their particular way of growth and the density of them. Governor Hamilton in 1790 mentions the 'many whim-

Floppers *An Asiatic plant that has taken to Bermuda, growing wild everywhere.*

Geranium *This was once trained upwards to form whole fences.*

Golden Shower *Suzette Lloyd's 'acacia bright with streaming gold'.*

Prickly pear *A plant which was of great interest to the first settlers.*

Poinciana *A native of Madagascar it grows gloriously in Bermuda.*

Pride of India *A native of Persia, it is one of the most common trees in Bermuda.*

Rosemary *Bermuda's best known and most useful herb.*

Palmetto *A good example of the decorative use of the palmetto.*

Surinam cherries   One of the most common hedges in Bermuda.

Sword tree   First introduced in 1826 this specimen was planted in 1911 to celebrate the coronation of King George V.

Tamarisk   This is known locally as 'spruce'.

Vitex   Nathaniel Tucker's 'lilac' and still called that locally.

Yucca *This escaped to grow happily along the seashore.*

Bermuda cedar *This old tree has managed to survive all the vicissitudes of the centuries, even the blight of the 1940s.*

Scarlet cordia *A plant introduced in 1829 and used as street planting in modern Bermuda.*

Buttonwood *A native plant which is particularly salt resistant.*

Easter lilies   *Greatly appreciated in Bermuda, a field like this would have been a common sight at the time of the bulb trade.*

Ginger   *This is used for decorative planting only in modern Bermuda.*

Red hibiscus   *A plant used for many hedges in both fields and gardens.*

Ipecacuanha   *This grows wild and attracts big orange butterflies.*

Honeysuckle   *Nathaniel Tucker's 'earth-born woodbines'.*

Mahogany   *This tree was originally grown for the use made of the wood.*

Oleander   *Another widely-used hedging plant.*

Olive   *Not all trees fruit in Bermuda and no use is made of the fruit when they do.*

Queen of shrubs *There are a few large old trees and many smaller shrubs. They bloom profusely.*

Allamanda *One of the many pretty vines growing in Bermuda.*

Allspice *Now growing wild in great profusion, allspice is used locally instead of bay for cooking.*

Red aloe *This is known locally as the 'Christmas aloe' for its time of flowering.*

Bermudiana *Truly Bermuda's national flower, it grows wild in both gardens and along sand dunes.*

Bignonia *This colourful plant grows well in Bermuda.*

Elder *A plant popular in Bermuda for its medicinal uses.*

Fennel *Originally a trade plant, fennel now grows wild everywhere.*

sical appearances' due to the way cedars rooted in the rock and that cedar brush could be trenched in as a manure or in the form of ash. He also says, 'the legislature has held out premiums for the planting of Cedar'. Suzette Lloyd's account is one of the nicest: '. . . for it forms entire groves and clothes all the vallies and hills from the water's edge to their very summit . . . height of about forty feet . . . only in sheltered and more cultivated spots is it relieved by brighter and fuller foliage of other trees.' It was used for furniture making as well as building. The dust put on a fire was considered to be purifying in the case of sickness: it was also put in pot-pourris and on the navel of newborn babies. The berries were made into cough syrup. A 'brush' was used to clean mould from hams and finally a dye can be obtained from the berries — either dull yellow or brown or khaki according to the mordant.

Ceiba pentandra	Silk cotton tree
CELERY *Apium graveolens*	One of Thomas Parson's plants in 1762. 'Salary'; Governor Hamilton lists it amongst his *Roots* in 1790.
CENTAURY *Gentiana nana*	Branching centaury. Is in F.A. Michaux's list of plants in 1806.
CENTURY PLANT *Agave americana*	In 1829 Suzette Lloyd mentions it as growing in Warwick and that its nickname was 'bamboo'. Being full of juice it, together with sand, would make a good lather for scrubbing floors.
Chaetochloa verticillata	Foxtail grass [Britton]
CHASTE TREE *Vitex agnus- castus*	Its name comes from the old use of the tree. If the leaves were put under a mattress the occupant slept peacefully, free from 'wicked unchaste dreams' and 'when eaten by wicked unchaste people, make them chaste like lambs'. The first mention of it in Bermuda is in 1772 in Nathaniel Tucker's poem 'The Bermudian'. It is probably his 'lilac'.
Citharexylum spinosum	Fiddlewood
CITRON *Citrus medica*	Rough skin lemon. Daniel Tucker lists this in 1616. Governor Robinson in 1687 mentions it as one of the many plants that grew so well but by his day had been 'blasted'. Suzette Lloyd in 1829 says it was flourishing in Walsingham.
Citrus aurantiifolia	Lime

Citrullus lanatus	Water melon
Citrus sp.	Orange
Citrus maxima	Shaddock
Citrus medica	Citron — Rough lemon
CLOVER *Medicago lupulina*	Governor Hamilton lists this amongst his *Grasses* in 1790 and F.A. Michaux in 1806 mentions this in his list of plants and says 'each stalk scarcely occupies an inch of ground, this is the most common plant of the country'. He goes on to say that the cows grazed from it.
Coccoloba uvifera	Bay grape
COCHINEAL PLANT *Nopalea cochinellifera*	This plant is very similar to the local prickly pear and in Norwood's *Journal* of 1631 he gives a dissertation on the similarities and the use the Mexican Indians made of it for dyeing. In fact true cochineal comes from a small, dark brown, tick-like creature which feeds on this cactus. Only the female is used. It is boiled just enough to make it swell then dried and minute red crystals are extracted to make carmine and crimson dyes. Suzette Lloyd mentions this cactus as growing here in 1829 and calls it *Cactus cochinellifera*.
COCOA *Eulophia* sp.	Suzette Lloyd is the only one to mention this being here but she wrote in 1829 'amid plantations of palmetto, aloes and cocoa'.
COFFEE	Both the wild coffee — *Psychotria ligustrifolia* and *Coffea arabica* grow in Bermuda according to Britton, in very much the same areas, i.e. Castle Harbour and Harrington Sound. There is no importation date for it. Governor Hamilton lists it in 1790 and Suzette Lloyd mentions 'deterioration of soil, where formerly grew . . . coffee'. In 1868 coffee was growing wild but this may have been the wild coffee and perhaps it was the cultivated variety that Miss Lloyd was talking about.
Colocasia esculenta	Eddo
COMFREY *Symphytum officinale*	The herbalists Gerard and Culpepper said this herb was good for spitting blood and knowing this makes the remarks of young Daniel Wadsworth in 1792 more explicable. He had brought his sister here suffering from consumption. He notes there is very little 'cumphrey' here and requests his father to send some together with other herbs for a recipe that was recommended to him for his sister.

Conocarpus erecta	Buttonwood
Cordia sebestena	Scarlet cordia
COREN CURINTH VINE	William Harrison writing in the late sixteenth century said 'since we traded to Zante [one of the Ionian Islands] the plant that beareth the Coren is also brought into this realm and although it bring not fruit to perfection, yet it may serve for pleasure and for some use, like as our vines do, though the climat so cold will not permit us to have good wines of them'. The first mention of this vine in Bermuda is in the *Rich Papers* in 1617 when a request is made for them to be procured from a 'Turkie Merchante' in London; the next in 1625 appears in a letter from the Company to Woodhouse saying they had been sent previously. William Harrison provides the reason why they should be tried here, like so many crops and they would have been used in the sweet/sour cookery.
CORIANDER *Coriander sativum*	A herb used for thousands of years and taken to Mexico by the Spanish, it is used in cooking. Perhaps one of Sir George Somers' 'kitchen herbs'. Britton refers to it growing wild prior to 1877 and at other times so we can presume it was an 'escape'.
CORN *Zea mays*	The words corn and wheat seem to have been used interchangeably in the early accounts with indian corn to describe maize. The earliest mention is in 1610 another in 1612 when it is described as one of the crops grown by the three men left on Bermuda at the departure of the *Deliverance* and the *Patience*. There is a story in 1619 of how corn left unhusked by the lazy survived the weevils better than that husked by the virtuous. In 1639 a shipwrecked Spaniard describes how corn was grown in each little farm and there was plenty. However by 1792 Daniel Wadsworth was complaining how little there was and how expensive.
CORAL TREE *Erythrina corallodendron*	Sword tree Suzette Lloyd is the first person to mention this in 1829. She called it the coral tree but gave it its correct Latin name. She says it was no more than eight or nine feet high, so it must have been a comparatively new introduction then. Today other trees are called coral trees here.
COTTON *Gossypium*	In 1632 cotton was ordered to be planted on every share of land. A hundred years later an Act was passed, in 1735, to encourage the planting of 'cotton-wool' and Governor Popple continued the encouragement. It had been tried on Smith's Island and at Walsingham by 1765, not very successfully. Governor Browne, armed with instructions from the King to grow cotton, had 40 acres planted in Tucker's Town in 1781. He described the

difficulties, particularly the wind and salt spray and how hedges did not give enough protection, and the lack of tall trees. Cotton was also planted at Port Royal in 1786 and by 1789, in spite of the difficulties and, according to Browne the 'natives engrossed in ship-building and salt raking', there were reckoned to be 33,000 plants. Governor Hamilton saw it and so did Suzette Lloyd in 1829 but only as 'hedges' in Somerset. The crop was woven and dyed at Ireland Island and though it declined as a crop until it was just growing wild by 1868, nevertheless Bermuda cotton won a prize at the Great Exhibition in London in 1851.

CRAB GRASS *Stenotaphrum secondatum*	There was little grass in 1603 according to a Spaniard who landed briefly in Bermuda but this grass was in a plant list of 1734 by Revd Clerk and Governor Hamilton in 1790 gives a short list of various grasses; this is one. Suzette Lloyd gives its Latin name as *Agrostis virginica* in 1829.
Crepe myrtle *Lagerstroemia indica*	
Crescentia cujete	Calabash
Crocus sativus	Saffron
CUCUMBER *Cucumis sativus*	One of the first vegetables to be planted here. To quote Silvester Jourdan in 1613 '. . sowed divers sortes of seeds to make trial of the ground . . . sprung up the fourth day after their sowing and amongst the rest of the seeds, the cowcumber and the mellon were forward'; they were still growing in 1790.
Cucumis melo	Melon
Cucurbita sp.	Gourd, Pumpkin
CUMIN *Cuminum cyminum*	Instructions for the growing of cumin appear in those to Governor Daniel Tucker in 1616. Cumin was valued for the same reasons as dill and anise, as a digestive and for various medicinal uses. It was also used as a flavouring for poultry and pickles but it needs a warmer climate than England and so if it succeeded in Bermuda it would be 'very good merchandise to be sent for England'.
Cycas revoluta	Sago palm
Cymbopogon citratus	Lemon grass
Cynara scolymus	Artichoke

DAHLIA sp.

Amongst Governor Reid's papers is an account of prizes being offered for various plants at the first Agricultural Show in 1843 and the dahlia is one of them; presumably the list is what could be expected to be growing and shown. Dahlias come from Mexico and had been first brought to England in 1789. They became a popular Victorian flower.

DANDELION
Taraxacum officinale

This humble plant is first mentioned in Bermuda by F.A. Michaux in 1806 but once it was a salad plant and magenta dye can be obtained from its roots.

Darrell's fleabane
Erigeron darrellanius

DATE PALM
Phoenix dactylifera

In 1687 there is an account of there having been plenty of these once but by then decreased in number. However when Governor Pitt's daughter went to see Colonel Byrd of Virginia in 1730 he suggested replanting. This was done and Suzette Lloyd saw them in 1829.

Datura suaveolens

Angel's trumpet — Brugmansia

Datura Stramonium and Datura tatula

Prickly burr, Thornapple, Jimson Weed. Thornapple was introduced into Jamestown, Virginia in 1603. It can be used as a painkiller but it is very poisonous and because of this Governor John Heydon issued an Order in 1678 to 'exterpate a bad and stinking weed ... which if suffered to grow may be very destructive to the Inhabitants of these Islands ...'.

Daucus carota

Carrot

Delonix regia

Royal poinciana

Dioscorea

Yam

DOCK
Rumex

In nineteenth century St David's (and no doubt in the rest of Bermuda)the leaves were used to wash dishes.

Dolichos lablab

Bonavista bean

EASTER LILY *Lilium longiflorum*	It is popularly believed that these lilies were introduced either in the eighteenth or very early nineteenth century. L.H. Smith researched their story very carefully and in her book *Bermuda's Oldest Inhabitants* she tells it. She gives the date as 1856. They are Japanese plants and it must be remembered that Japan was largely shut to plant explorers until the middle of the last century. This flower was only taken to Europe in 1830, so I am sure 1856 is correct. She goes on to give the history of the trade in Easter lilies.
EDDOWS Eddoe Coco *Colocasia esculenta*	A West Indian edible tuber. First mentioned as growing here by Governor Hamilton in 1790. Governor Reid had it on his list for prizes for the first Agricultural Show in 1843.
ELDER *Sambucus* sp.	This plant has many medicinal uses and a tea is drunk in Bermuda. It is said it never sets fruit here as it does elsewhere. It will also give a blue and lavender dye. No import date.
Erigeron darrellanius	Darrell's fleabane
Eriobotrya japonica	Loquat
Erythrina corallodendron	Coral tree — Sword tree
EUCALYPTUS sp.	The tree may be seen occasionally in Bermuda. It is mentioned by Lefroy, Britton and L.H. Smith but there is no import date.
Eugenia axillaris	Stopper
Eugenia uniflora	Surinam cherry
Eulophia sp.	Cocoa
Euphorbia ipecacuanha	Ipecacuanha
Euphorbia pulcherrima	Poinsettia

'FATHER JOHN'
Red justicia
Justicia secunda

No book about the plants of Bermuda could possibly be without a reference to this herb, such a favourite is it of Bermudians. It is just about good for everything. The leaves are boiled down to make a tea, it goes a red colour and may be drunk hot or cold. It is a native of the West Indies and has locally escaped here from cultivation to grow wild. Apart from Britton mentioning it in 1918 we have no way of knowing when it came to Bermuda.

FENNEL
Foeniculum vulgare

The seeds were used on fast days to allay pangs of hunger and even the Puritans permitted themselves to eat them during long sermons. Amongst the seeds sent to Daniel Tucker for cultivation in 1616. Bermuda proved to be an ideal habitat for it. This must have been known in the early years for in 1658 a request came from Barbados for fennel seed. It now grows wild. Fennel has many of the same properties as anise but is stronger in its growth. Gerard said of it that it was good for nursing mothers, for digestion and the 'wamblings' of the stomach. A local use is fennel tea for 'breaking temperatures'. It is a traditional seasoning for fat meat such as pork and oily fish.

Ficus elastica
Rubber tree

It is reported to have been imported by the Governor's lady of the day, Lady Turner in 1826. The best known one is that at Par-le-Ville, planted by Mr Perot in 1834.

FIDDLEWOOD
*Citharexylum
spinosum*

First planted in Bermuda in 1830 at Paynter's Vale, it is a native of the West Indies. Locally it was used as a dressing for shoes. Mash the leaves and rub on brown shoes for preserving the leather and shine.

FIGS
Ficus carica

It is possible that the Spanish who landed before Sir George Somers may have left figs behind, as they did the olive. Certainly by 1616 Daniel Tucker issued a proclamation against thieving of figs and by 1617 Robert Rich had planted fig trees round his well and was planning to use them as a fence, quite a common practice at the time. He said that if he had had a means of preserving them he would have sent a ship load back to England. By 1623 a method had been found — drying frames set up, the feet of which had been dipped in tar. The Spaniard who left us a description of Bermuda in 1639 said there were 'countless groves of fig trees, . . . able to pick fruit, figs small and all the more delicious because not cultivated'. By 1762 Thomas Parsons lists figs as one of the summer fruits and Philip Freneau in 1778 also lists figs amongst other things. By 1784 it could be said 'each under his own vine and fig tree, the fruit of the latter being at this time in great variety, plenty and perfection'. Governor Hamilton merely mentions them as one of many fruit trees in 1790 as does Suzette Lloyd in 1829.

FLAX
Linum usitatissimum

Amongst Captain Roger Wood's letters of 1632 is the following request: 'if you please to send us half bushell of Hempseed and as much Flaxseed I hope we shall make good use of it'. By 1644 on 9th June an Order was given '. . . said Mr Watlington doe with his own hands weave twenty yard of brode linen cloth'. About that time young people were being apprenticed as weavers. However it is a crop that needs a great deal of water in its preparation to make cloth, being soaked either in ditches or barrels, so possibly this is why it never became an export crop for Bermuda. Like many other plants it has several uses, both medicinal and practical. The seed was used in poultices and for calf food. The oil was made into a cake with honey to lick to ease coughs. It was also used by artists.

FLEABANE
Darrell's fleabane
Erigeron darrellanius

It was amongst the first collection of plants to be sent to England in 1699 to Mr Petiver by John Dickinson, and it was on the list of the next plant collector Revd Clerk in 1734. It is an endemic plant of Bermuda. Fleabane in England was gathered and burned to exterminate fleas; it was a strewing herb and was used for scouring floors. It was not named 'Darrell's' until the nineteenth century for the man who helped Lefroy with his work on Bermudian plants.

FLOPPERS
Life plant
Byrophyllum pinnatum

A far eastern plant, it was brought back to Bermuda in 1813.

FOXTAIL GRASS
Chaetochloa verticillata

A grass of Europe, it was in the list of *Grasses* made by Governor Hamilton in 1790.

Fragaria

Strawberry

FUSCHIA sp.
'*grandiflora*' and '*globosa*'

Amongst the classes for which prizes were offered at the first Agricultural Show in 1843 were two for these fuschias. The fuschia had been known since the early eighteenth century but it was not until around 1830 that it came into commercial cultivation in England.

Galium bermudense	Bedstraw
Gentiana nana	Centaurium — Branching centaury

GERANIUMS

These are a descendant of the cranesbill family. Both geraniums and cranesbills were grown in sixteenth, seventeenth and eighteenth century English gardens. Scented geraniums in fact came from South Africa albeit as early as 1690 and 1774. The first mention of the geranium in Bermuda is by F.A. Michaux in 1806, in the little gardens of St George's. He says 'geranium roseum et zonale'. At that date all geraniums and pelargoniums were lumped together as 'geranium', it was only later the different names were applied. 'Zonale' means the faint shadowy line found on some leaves; 'roseum' probably meant a deep pink, but by now it is not known what exactly was meant. Suzette Lloyd in 1829 refers to geraniums 'which form entire hedges eight or ten feet high'. The explanation of this is that indeed at that date they were trained up trellises and could grow to twenty feet and live many years. They were a favourite flower but it was not until 1844 that the dwarf bedding geranium was introduced for general cultivation.

GINGER
Zingiber officinalis

One solitary mention of this plant — an Act passed in 1735 for the encouragement to plant ginger plus other plants. It was much used for seasoning both in sweet/sour dishes and savoury ones.

GOLDEN ROD
*Solidago
  sempervirens*

A native of Bermuda, being a North American plant. It can be used as a dye plant.

GOLDEN SHOWER
Cassia fistula

A tree known to Gerard and with medicinal uses. Suzette Lloyd in 1829 writes 'delicate acacia bright with streaming gold'. Acacia was applied to several trees in the eighteenth and nineteenth centuries but not usually to cassias. Perhaps for once she made a mistake. This tree does seem to be the most likely candidate for her comment.

Gossypium sp.

Cotton

GOURD *Cucurbita* sp.	One of the vegetables mentioned by Governor Hamilton in his list of 1790 but he does not say which type. Bottle gourds were brought by the Garrison in the 1850s.
Grapes, vines *Vitis*	
GRANADILLA	In 1790 Governor Hamilton mentions this. It may be Suzette Lloyd's 'Water lemon' or yellow granadilla — *Passiflora laurifolia*, or it may be something else.
GROUNDNUT *Arachis hypogea*	Also seen by Suzette Lloyd in 1829 who gave the same Latin name.
Guava *Psidium* sp.	
Guaiacum officinale Lignum Vitae	
Gum Copal West Indian locust *Hymenaea* *Courbaril*	

HEMP *Cannabis sativa*	The other half of Captain Roger Wood's order in 1632 — 'if you please to send us half bushell of Hempseed and as much Flaxseed'. Hemp was used not only for ropes but also for tough working clothes. Gerard made the comment: 'Bad for men but good to make hens lay more plentifully'. Another crop that needs a lot of water in its preparation, which must have presented difficulties to the early colonists.
HERBS	One word to cover such a large selection of plants because many that we no longer use were of use to people of previous centuries. The very first mention of 'kitchen herbs' was in 1609 when Sir George Somers planted out his garden very soon after his arrival.

It may well have contained our kitchen herbs but it equally could have had violets and marigolds in addition. Eighty years later Governor Robinson says in 1687 there were 'no poisonous herbs' and that 'sundry [people] resorting to ye Churchyard for pott herbs'. We do know rosemary, sweet marjoram and marigolds were grown in churchyards.

HIBISCUS	It is a family name that has been applied to many different plants and it is hard for us to know now what Revd Clerk meant when he sent a 'small hibiscus' in his collection of plants from Bermuda in 1734. Suzette Lloyd in 1829 describes the *Hibiscus mutabilis* or changeable rose very clearly and gives *Flos hororius* as another name for it. She says, 'flowers white changing to pink to purple during day, hollyhock like flowers, [bush] twelve feet high'. *Hibiscus rosa-sinensus* is known as the shoe black plant, the flowers being crushed and used for shoe cleaning — it is also a dye plant.
Hibiscus tiliaceus Mahoe	According to Lefroy seeds of this tree were washed ashore in 1825 and there was a very large tree at Somerville in Smith's prior to 1879.
HONEYSUCKLE *Lonicera japonica* and *Lonicera* *sempervirens*	The yellowy white and the red honeysuckle both grow here. The old name for it was 'woodbine' and Nathaniel Tucker says in his poem of 1772 'the Earthborn woodbines on the surface creep' and Suzette Lloyd in 1829 refers to the 'clustering woodbine'.
Hordeum sp.	Barley
HOREHOUND *Marrubium* *vulgare*	We have no import date for this but since it had several uses in old Bermuda it may well have been an early import. For a poor appetite boil the leaves, sweeten and sip slowly. It was also used with mint in hens' nests to keep away maywings. In other places it was used as a cough remedy in the form of sweets.
Hymenaea courbaril Locust Gum copal West Indian locust	This large tree was brought to Bermuda towards the end of the seventeenth century. It is from Barbados and was valued for the 'finest, transparent varnish' that it provided. There was a large one at Cavendish House in Devonshire under which Whitfield, the Methodist, preached in 1748. By 1829 when Suzette Lloyd saw the tree it was sixteen feet in circumference. She also saw trees growing at the Tuckers' house, 'The Grove', at Port Royal and Governor Hamilton had seen locust trees in 1790. At one time they were planted about the public buildings in Hamilton.
Hymenocallis *declinata*	Spider lily

INDIGO
Indigofera

Five different types of indigo give the dye. The English planters in America used the Guatemala indigo so perhaps it was used in Bermuda too. Britton claims the indigo seen growing wild today is not the *Indigofera tinctoria*. It was growing by 1623 and it was obviously hoped to make a good cash crop of it. However it needs good, rich, level soil, not too dry. It robs and impoverishes ground and must be grown alone and free of weeds. Caterpillars are a great pest to it. It has to be steeped in at least three separate vats of water and after maceration the resulting powder has to be dried out of the sun and rain. It needs frequent pruning for the colour comes from the leaves not the stalks, so young succulent plants are best. All this must have been difficult. But it was still being grown in 1645 and 1648 and was used as payment. Governor Hamilton saw it in 1790 and by 1829 Suzette Lloyd said there were plantations of it in Walsingham which were growing well. By 1868 it was growing wild. It is one of the oldest of dyes and though it dyes blue, with heat and different mordants it will dye pink, lavender or tan. In Barbados it was used to dye paper blue in order to wrap sugar loaves as it was considered an insect repellent.

INDIGO, Wild
Baptisia tinctoria
Horsefly weed

In 1616 there is a mention of 'Indigo — an esculant'. It is a north-eastern American plant which resembles asparagus for which it was used as a substitute in New England. However, it is poisonous to animals. It has a medicinal use against acne.

IPECACUANHA
*Euphorbia
  ipecacuanha*

Governor Hamilton mentions this in his list of 1790. Suzette Lloyd says it was growing in Somerset in 1829 — 'three feet high with orange flowers'. It was valued for the emetic and purgative properties of its roots.

Ipomoea batatas

Sweet potato

Ipomoea dissecta

Noyau vine

JASMINE
Jasminum sp.

Another of the plants mentioned in Nathaniel Tucker's poem of 1772 but Suzette Lloyd in 1829 differentiated between an 'Arabian jessamine' to which she gave the name '*Nyctanthis*' and said it had pink blossoms on a tree, and 'jessamine' in a list of smaller plants. According to L.H. Smith, *Jasmine simplicifolium* was first planted in Paynter's Vale by Archdeacon Spencer in 1840. It is now a rampant weed in Walsingham.

Jimson weed
Datura stramonium
    and *Datura tatula*

JUMBEY
Leucaena glauca

No import date for this but a widely spread weed. In the Bahamas it is used to cure wind on the stomach, quiet nerves and treat heart trouble.

Juniperus
    bermudiana

Bermuda cedar

Justicia secunda

'Father John'

KOHLRABI
Brassica oleracea

Amongst Governor Reid's list of vegetables in 1843.

Lactuca sativa	Lettuce
Lagenaria siceraria	Bottle gourd
Lagerstroemia indica	Crepe myrtle — Queen of shrubs — Pride of India. André Michaux father of F.A. Michaux is reputed to have taken this shrub to America in 1785, and like so much else it probably came to Bermuda very soon after from America.
Lantana involucrata	Sage bush — *Lantana camara* — Ornamental sage bush The wild bush was brought from the Bahamas by Samuel Spofferth some time between 1739 and 1750. His idea was that it could be used for firewood. However it was merely useful for kindling. F.A. Michaux saw it in 1806, calling it *Lantana involucrata* and commenting on its aromatic leaf. By 1829 Suzette Lloyd said 'Land usurped by *Lantana salvifolia*'. The decorative *Lantana camara* had been brought from Madeira in 1819. The leaves are used as a toothbrush locally and it is interesting that the proper sage was used in the same way 300 years ago in England. Together with cedar, a tea can be made against yellow fever because it induces a sweat.
LAVENDER *Lavendula* sp.	Governor Hamilton lists this in 1790 but frustratingly just puts 'etc.' after it, thinking no doubt no one would be interested in the rest of the herbs. Maybe it was one of the 'sweet smelling herbs of the kind found in Spain' that the shipwrecked Spaniard saw in 1639.
LEMON *Citrus limon*	Governor Daniel Tucker was sent seeds of lemons in 1616, with instructions how to treat the seedlings. By 1638 they had become so prolific that they could be used for paying rents. This plenty is confirmed by the Spaniard in 1639 when he says, 'In most farms orange and lemon trees, very beautiful large fruit.' By 1687 however Governor Robinson wrote sadly that where there had been vast numbers of lemons and other fruit they had all been 'blasted'. Like other plants, however, by 1762 Thomas Parsons was writing 'and in the fall of the year we ship of an immense number of . . . lemons . . . to North America'. In spite of the poverty and near starvation of 1772 Henry Tucker endeavoured to send a barrel of oranges and lemons to brother St

George in Williamsburg. Governor Hamilton listed lemons amongst his trees in 1790 and Daniel Wadsworth commented '...lemons without number'. Suzette Lloyd saw them growing in Walsingham in 1829 and by 1868 they were still regarded as one of the principal productions of Bermuda.

LEMON GRASS
Cymbopogon citratus

It is a herb used in Far Eastern cookery. It is thought it was taken from the Far East to South America by the Portuguese and Spanish. Certainly it is used for 'Montezuma's Revenge' in Mexico in the form of a tea today. In Bermuda it is steeped in boiling water, strained and sugar added to be used like lemonade for coughs.

LETTUCE
Lactuca sativa

The first person to plant this was Sir George Somers in his garden in August 1609. It very probably was one of the plants included in Thomas Parsons' and Governor Hamilton's 'salleting'. Gerard has to say of it that it was used against heartburn, as an appetiser as a first course but when eaten as last course 'keepeth away drunkenness by reason it stayeth the vapours from rising up to the head'. He then quoted a sad little rhyme from an elderly man:
'Tell me why lettuce which our grandsires last did eat,
Is now of late become to be the first of meate.'
Ever was it so, that fashions in eating change.

Life Plant, Floppers
Byrophyllum pinnatum

LIGNUM VITAE
Guaiacum officinale

In Silvester Jourdan's account of 1613 of the discovery and plants of Bermuda he postulates that one of the unknown trees might have been this. It grows in the Bahamas so it might have been brought on wind and tide. Britton lists it as being in a few gardens.

Lilium longiflorum

Easter lily

LIME
Citrus aurantiifolia

Has a very similar history to lemons. The first limes were brought in at the same time as the other citrus and by 1635 there is a description of the *Rebecca* arriving in Massachusetts Bay with a load of limes, together with other fruits from Bermuda. They were part of the exports to North America in 1762 that Thomas Parsons listed and Daniel Wadsworth said that they were without number in 1792. They were one of Governor Hamilton's trees in 1790. Suzette Lloyd in 1829 saw limes in Walsingham and at 'The Grove' in Port Royal 'in scattered clumps with other trees'. In the Bahamas it is said the juice will keep mosquitoes away and if applied to a bite will cure the itch.

Linum *usitatissimum*	Flax
LITCHI CHINENSIS	In 1853 Governor Elliott planted these to see how they would grow.
Locust West Indian locust *Hymenaea courbaril*	
Lonerica sp.	Honeysuckle
LOQUAT *Eriobotrya japonica*	In 1850 Governor Reid introduced the loquat as one of his new plants.
Lycopersicon	Tomato

MADDER *Rubia tinctorum*	In Captain John Smith's *Review of the State of the Plantation* of 1622 he mentions how it is expected that with the cultivation of certain crops prosperity can be hoped for — one of those crops was madder. It is one of the oldest dyes of all and is of the same family as bedstraw. After three years growth it is dug out for its roots which are cleaned, dried and ground and then dried again. It will dye various shades of red according to the mordant used. By 1772 it was still regarded as an important crop, although not in Bermuda. The Dutch had captured the market and were raising the price. Like many plants it had its medicinal uses too — against bruising and miscarriages.
Mahoe *Hibiscus tiliaceus*	
MAHOGANY *Swietenia mahagoni*	In 1734 Revd Clerk who sent a collection of plants from Bermuda to England included mahogany amongst them.
MAIZE *Zea mays* Indian corn	This was loosely referred to as corn or indian corn in the early years. The term maize seems to have come later. Captain John Smith in 1623 makes it quite clear when he writes, 'the Corne is the same they have in Virginia and the West Indies' and says

there can be two harvests a year. By 1687 however Governor Robinson wrote the soil would be very productive if it was manured and that the inhabitants dig with hoes and plant indian corn. By 1718 it was necessary to pass an Act for the greater encouragement to grow the crop. Governor Hamilton listed it as one of the grains in 1790. F.A. Michaux observed the lack of agriculture in 1806 although he did admit vegetables and maize were grown. Suzette Lloyd commented in 1829 'deterioration of soil where formerly grew Indian corn'.

Malus sp.	Apple
MAMEE APPLE *Mammea americana*	It is not a popular tree here but Suzette Lloyd saw this growing in Walsingham in 1829 and there is a tree at Orange Grove, Smith's, planted certainly by 1872.
MANGO *Mangifera indica*	This was one of Governor Elliott's contributions in 1853.
MANGROVE *Rhizophora mangle* and Black Mangrove *Avicennia nitida*	Mangroves caused interested comments from the first people to arrive. Silvester Jourdan writing in 1613 says 'a kinde of tree called mangrowes, they grow very strangely and would make a man wonder to see the manner of their growing'. By 1790 however Governor Hamilton merely lists them amongst 'Forest trees'. Suzette Lloyd in 1829 mentions that Mangrove Bay was completely overgrown with mangroves. The plant has its uses. At one time it was used for dyeing and dressing leather as it contains tannin. The wood was used for wheels and certainly in the nineteenth century fishermen coloured their lines with dye from the shoots.
Manihot esculente	Cassava
Maranta arundinacea	Arrowroot
MARJORAM *Origanum majorana*	The instructions to Governor Daniel Tucker in 1616 mention marjoram amongst the other seeds sent with the further observation that the roots will survive from year to year and only the tops must be taken for further seed. By the early eighteenth century it was being planted on the graves and it was still flourishing in the nineteenth century in St David's. Its medicinal use was for children with colic.
MARIGOLDS *Calendula officinalis*	Also planted on graves in the early eighteenth century; one of the 'pott herbs' mentioned by Governor Robinson.
Marrubium vulgare	Horehound
Medicago lupulina	Clover

MELLILOT	One of the plants sent by John Dickinson to England in his collection of 1699. Listed by Governor Hamilton amongst his Grasses in 1790.
Melia azedarach	Pride of India
Melocactus communis	Turk's cap cactus
MELON *Cucumis melo*	From the very beginning of the colony both water and musk-melons have been planted. Captain John Smith makes this very clear in 1623, but the account of 1612 about the three men who had been left on Bermuda at the departure of the *Deliverance* and the *Patience* merely says they had planted melons. Governor Hamilton in 1790 comments that there are both musk- and water-melons.
MERCURY *Rhus radicans*	Herb mercury — Stinkweed Although F.A. Michaux's account of 1806 does not leave us a long list this plant is on it and it is the first mention.
MILLETT *Panicum miliaceum* sp.	In 1790 Governor Hamilton lists this amongst his *Grains*.
MINT *Mentha* sp.	There is no importation date for mint which now grows wild all over Bermuda. However in nineteenth century St David's it was used with horehound to keep maywings away from hens' nests. It is also made into a decoction for 'cleaning the blood' today.
MULBERRY *Morus* sp.	There has been discussion that the first colonists did not in fact find the true mulberry growing when they arrived but called the prickly pear the mulberry. Sylvester Jourdan's account of 1610 leaves no doubt there were both red and white mulberries as well as prickly pears. Seeds of mulberry were sent to Daniel Tucker in 1616 complete with instructions as to how the seedlings should subsequently be treated. Captain John Smith also gives a separate description of the prickly pear in 1623, having already mentioned the mulberry. In 1625 the Bermuda Company sent seeds of the black mulberry, recommending them highly, saying, 'It is the same fruit as whereof in Spayne they make there great quantities of Alicant wyne' which was then exported to England and elsewhere. They also said they would endeavour to send some already rooted and growing trees, although they were very expensive and difficult to get. All this interest was of course in the hope of fostering a silk trade because they sent silk worms as well. The trees lived on, for Governor Hamilton listed mulberries in 1790 and so did Suzette Lloyd in 1829.

MULLEIN *Verbascum thapsus*	Hag's taper — Aaron's rod are some of its folk names. The first mention is by F.A. Michaux in 1806 but it was growing wild at Boaz and Ireland Islands in the 1850s. It has a long history of medicinal use as a cough remedy for both cattle and people.
Musa sp.	Bananas and plantains.
MUSK-MELON *Cucumis melo*	Gerard has a drawing and description of the musk-melon. It is more deeply indented than other types, a russet and green colour with a paler yellow flesh. Sir George Somers planted these in his first garden of August 1609 and Captain John Smith noted there were plenty growing in 1623. Thomas Parsons in 1762 lists them as one of the summer fruits and Governor Hamilton saw them in 1790. The true cantaloupe came from Armenia and in eighteenth century garden lists in America 'cantaloupe' and 'musk melon' are listed separately.

NASTURTIUM *Tropaeolum*	Indian cress A native of South America nevertheless it was well known in the late sixteenth century. Nathaniel Tucker is the first person to mention it here in his poem of 1772. It was used in salads. It was not as widespread here in Bermuda even a hundred or seventy years ago as it is today. Its escape is fairly recent.
NETTLE *Urtica*	F.A. Michaux in 1806 gives us the first mention of nettles. They became a medicinal remedy for measles being steeped in boiling water, the result cooled and used to bathe patients. Nettle tea was also used for 'breaking temperatures'. It gives a greeny-yellow dye.
Nicotiana tabaccum	Tobacco
Nopalea cochinellifera	Cochineal plant
NOYAU *Ipomoea dissecta* [Britton]	One of the vines mentioned by Suzette Lloyd in 1829 as being in the garden of 'Roselands', the house where she stayed.
Nyctanthes arbor-tristis	Night-flowering jasmine

OATS *Avena sativa*	One of the list of Governor Hamilton's observed grains in 1790.
Ocimum basilicum	Basil
OLEANDER *Nerium oleander*	According to L.H. Smith a Mr Lightbourn of Paget was responsible for bringing the oleander to Bermuda from Charleston in 1790. Suzette Lloyd saw it in 1829 and gave it the name of 'Southsea Rose'.
OLIVE *Olea europea*	Was found growing here by the crew of the *Sea Venture* and, as it is not a native, it is presumed that the Spanish who landed during the sixteenth century must have planted it. However it has never produced fruit in a sufficient quantity to be a cash crop. The trees live to be very old. It is mentioned in Nathaniel Tucker's poem of 1772 and Governor Hamilton saw trees in 1790. Suzette Lloyd refers to the 'classic olive' in 1829 and it was growing at Walsingham.
OLIVEWOOD BARK *Cassine laneana*	One of Bermuda's endemic trees. Its bark may have been used for tanning by the first settlers. Another tree, the buttonwood, also produces bark suitable for the purpose. Certainly there were tanners and shoemakers by 1650 for there were complaints that their prices were too high and that they cut bark without permission.
ONIONS *Allium* sp.	Whatever else Bermuda has or has not been able to grow over the centuries it has been able to grow onions. Even at the lowest production time in the early eighteenth century onions were still exported. The first were planted by Sir George Somers in 1609. The Bermuda Company sent onion seed to Daniel Tucker in 1616 amongst others to be planted. By 1762 Thomas Parsons claimed that 'if our vessels have no very long passages they will clear by ducks and onions not less than three hundred to three hundred and fifty pounds a trip' (to the West Indies). Governor Hamilton lists them amongst his vegetables in 1790. Suzette Lloyd confirms the export of them in 1829 and says fifty acres were given to growing onions. By 1844 Sandys Parish alone was growing 200,700 lbs and the island altogether 332,735 lbs. By 1868 they were still listed as one of the principal productions.

They had been found to be anti-scorbutic and Captain Cook, by feeding his crew an onion a day, brought them home without scurvy, considered to be near miraculous then. The old Bermuda remedy for earache was to roast an onion, cut it up and put small pieces in the ear. It is a dye plant and with different mordants produces warm brown or yellow.

ORANGES
Citrus sp.

They have as long a history in Bermuda as onions. The first seeds were sent to Daniel Tucker for planting in 1616. So successful must they have been that by 1621 Governor Butler was able to include oranges in a chest of fruits sent as a present to Virginia. Rents were paid in oranges as well as tobacco. Some of these went to England in cedar boxes thereby achieving a double effect, i.e. exporting the cedar against the law. They were also part of some rent agreements, that land should be planted with oranges. The Spaniard who was wrecked in 1639 attests to the excellence of the fruit when he says, 'Lovely orange trees . . . In most of farms orange and lemon trees, very beautiful large fruit . . .'. However because of the tree cutting for ship-building and the removal of shelter there was a period when Governor Robinson in 1687 wrote that though there had been a vast number of oranges they had been blasted and only 'small, withered oranges' were left. By 1762 they were being exported again to North America and by 1773 Anne Tucker sent to St George, her brother in Williamsburg, a present of preserved oranges and Henry tried to send a barrel of oranges and lemons. His present of preserved oranges ended up with brother Tommy instead. If there had not been a scarcity of sugar more preserved oranges would have been sent. So it is predictable that Governor Hamilton should list them amongst his trees in 1790. Daniel Wadsworth comments in 1792 'Sower oranges grow wild in great abundance'. Suzette Lloyd in 1829 comments on the 'sweet orange', 'Big and good'. Admiralty House garden had plantations of oranges, so had Walsingham and at 'The Grove' at Port Royal, which belonged to the Tuckers, she saw orange trees amongst the other scattered clumps of trees. In 1839 Governor Reid, on his arrival, was very concerned with the state of the orange trees. Scale was a bad problem, originating in the West Indies. He entered into correspondence with the Horticultural Society in London, new seed was sent and by 1848 the new varieties were bearing fruit and increasing. Reid had wished that 'orange orchards may become something more than a luxury'. This had been achieved in spite of an intervening bad hurricane.

Origanum majorana

Sweet marjoram

OXALIS

Michaux in 1806 lists *Oxalis acetosella* and this is considered to be a mistake although a type of oxalis does grow in Bermuda.

PALMETTO
Sabal bermudana

One of Bermuda's endemic trees it caused favourable comment from the very beginning. The men saw the pigs eating the berries and willingly shared the harvest. Because of the popularity of them it enabled the flour that had been brought on the *Sea Venture* to be taken on to Virginia. The liquor obtained by boring a hole in the trunk was also considered delicious. The crown was eaten like a cabbage, the large leaves used for thatching and on occasions the leaves covered men at night or could be used like an umbrella. There was also an intoxicating liquor named 'Bibby' to be made from it. However it is a tree that grows extremely slowly and anxiety was felt about its destruction early on. Acts were passed in 1658, 1668 and 1772 against the destruction of the trees, to prevent fraud in measuring the plait and orders given to replant. The manufacture of plait from the leaves seems to have begun in the late 1600s. The first mention is by Governor Robinson in 1687. Baskets, mats, ropes, hats and bonnets were all made and exported. In England the hats became very fashionable for a short while. Governor Hope said in 1722 that he had difficulty in taxing the people because of the poverty and that plait might be taken in payment but he also said in 1724 he wondered how long the 'manufacture of platt' will last for 'in 60–70 years it is not perceived that any plant has advanced an inch'. Mark Catesby had made similar remarks ten years earlier. He added that the berries were made into buttons. The fashion for the hats must have been short-lived for Governor Pitt wrote to England in 1735 saying '. . . of the palmetto tree leaf they lately manufactured a platting for women's hats which proved of great use to the poor, of this commodity they some years ago shipped so much to Great Britain that has produced from eight to ten thousand pounds sterling but the price is so much fallen of late that its esteemed not worth the labour of making, whereby the poorer sort of inhabitants are reduced to great extremity'. Governor Hamilton in 1790 lists the palmetto amongst his trees but also says 'used for hats, baskets, mats and ropes'. Michaux noted its presence in 1806 and so did Suzette Lloyd in 1829 but with no further comment. In fact the manufacture just went quietly on till nearly the present day.

PALM
Roystonea

Royal palm   The first mention of this is in a letter dated 1772 from Henry Tucker to St George, his brother in Williamsburg, when he offers to send him seeds of the 'Palmetto Royal'. He had had a strange tree which had had two heads and plenty of seed.

Panicum miliaceum sp.	Millet

PARSLEY
Petroselenium crispum

There is no import date for this but it was certainly growing in St David's in the nineteenth century and it is to be found growing wild today in many places so it is one of Bermuda's 'escapes'. Medicinally it has diuretic properties and it is a dye plant.

PARSNIP
Pastinaca sativus

Amongst the first vegetables to be planted in 1610 according to L.H. Smith. Certainly by 1623 Captain John Smith listed them too. They played a large part in the diet of earlier centuries.

Parthenocissus quinquefolia

Virginia creeper

PASSION FLOWER

There are certainly two types that grow here. Suzette Lloyd in 1829 mentions that Walsingham was 'overgrown with passion flower'. Britton gives *Passiflora incarnata* as being a native and growing in Walsingham and other places not far from there so Miss Lloyd probably saw the same plant. Britton also says the fruit was known as 'apricot' in his day.

Passiflora laurifolia

Water lemon — Yellow granadilla

PAWPAW
Carica papaya

Henry May was shipwrecked on Bermuda in 1593 with a party of Frenchmen and one of the plants he saw was this. It may have been left by another shipwrecked party or perhaps arrived on the tide. The ship *Edwin* brought more up from the West Indies in 1616 and by 1621 the trees were producing so well that the fruit was included in a chestful of presents sent to Virginia. Gerard has a drawing of it in his *Herbal* of 1633 and calls it the Dug tree. Governor Hamilton noted it in 1790, Michaux in 1806 and Suzette Lloyd in 1829. It has also been regarded as a meat tenderiser, pieces being put in a stew, or the meat being wrapped in its leaves. It is one of the components of modern meat tenderisers. In old Bermuda the juice of the green fruit was used against ringworm and warts. In the Bahamas it is said to cure 'the plenty drink' feeling.

PEACH
Prunus persica

The first mention of this is by Governor Hamilton in 1790 and confirmed by Suzette Lloyd in 1829. W.F. Williams claimed it was introduced in the early 1800s but, though this is not accurate, he also said it was very successful by 1849. It can be a dye plant, giving a yellow dye from its leaves.

PEAS *Pisum sativum*	This was another important staple of earlier diets. Sir George Somers planted them in August 1609 in his garden and in the instructions sent to Daniel Tucker in 1616 were commands to plant them in the garden near a fort to provide food for the garrison. They were one of the successful crops listed by Captain Smith in 1623. Governor Hamilton in 1790 lists three different types: 'Peas . . . black-eyed peas and pigeon peas'. They used to be dried to take on long voyages.
Pelargonium	Geranium
PEPPER *Capsicum baccatum*	The bird pepper is native to Bermuda. The first comment was in 1612 by Silvanus Jourdan who says, '. . In some of our islands there grows Pepper but not so good as our Indian pepper.' Before the discovery of the Americas all pepper came from the Far East. Black and white pepper was known but the capsicum family came from the Americas and, as we know, has a different taste and type of pepperiness. Robert Rich in 1617 sent to Nathaniel, his brother, some 'of this Country pepper which bruised and taken with a cup of sack is good against the windiness of the stomach'. However 'red pepper' was sent off to Virginia in the chest of presents in 1621 and rents were paid in pepper as well as other crops, as noted in 1638. Suzette Lloyd comments on 'plantations of . . . pepper . . .' in 1829.
Persea persea	Avocado
Phaseolus sp.	Bean
Phaseolus limensis	Lima bean
Phoenix dactylifera	Date palm
Phyla nodiflora	Capeweed
Pimenta dioica (*officinalis*)	Allspice
Pimpinella anisum	Anise
PINEAPPLE *Ananas comosus*	First brought to Bermuda on the *Edwin* in 1616 from the West Indies. They flourished and Captain Smith referred to the 'most delicate pineapples' in 1623. Governor Roger Wood writes in 1633: 'I wish I could send 1,000 in their season to the Queen and 500 more to such as desire them, for I can well spare them and eat enough myself. I sent four boats laden this year unto the main, to give them to those good dames that love to eat them better than to plant them and I assure you I love to plant and

preserve them and behold them in their beauty more than to munch them alone without the company of my friends.' A rent agreement dated 1650 specified that pines should be planted, as well as other fruit. But the number grown declined as so much else did, so that by 1724 and 1730 Governors Hope and Pitt could write sadly they were grown no more though they had been renowned as 'the Best'. There were in fact a few being grown as they were listed in 1735 but that is the last mention of them.

PLANTAINS
Musa sp.

First brought to Bermuda in 1616 on the *Edwin* from the West Indies. They grew so successfully that in 1619 they were included in the chest of presents that went on the ship to Virginia. Philip Freneau wrote in 1778 that although they were growing in some places they were not common because of destruction by the wind, but Governor Hamilton listed them amongst his trees in 1790. Suzette Lloyd said in 1829 that they were in plantations in Admiralty House garden. Dwarf plantains (*Musa sapientum*) were imported from Cayenne via Demerara by Governor Reid in 1845 as part of his scheme for promoting agriculture.

PLANTAIN
Plantago major
Plantago lanceolata

'Rubark', 'Rhubarb', 'Cats cradle', Ribwort   With all their folk names it is obvious that these plants have been used from time immemorial for medicinal purposes. Michaux is the only person to have noted them in 1806 but the plant is very well known in Bermuda. Mashed in a saucer it is used for cuts and put with lard it may be used for a poultice.

POINCIANA
Delonix regia

This tree is a native of Madagascar and grows very well in Bermuda. L.H. Smith says it was brought to Bermuda in 1870 and planted at Mount Langton (Government House) but the tree at Orange Valley is purported to have been planted about 1830.

Poinciana
  pulcherrima
Caesalpinia
  pulcherrima

Barbados flower fence

POINSETTIA
Euphorbia
  pulcherrima

This plant was named after an American consul to Mexico. It must have arrived in Bermuda some time in the first half of the nineteenth century for it figures in collections of drawings and paintings of plants of about 1856.

POISON IVY
Rhus toxicodendron

Captain John Smith has a certain amount to say about this plant in 1623. He says that, though its effects are painful at the time, it leaves no lasting harm, which in fact is true! In 1620 John Dutton in a letter to Sir Nathaniel Rich noted: 'I have sent you the poyson weed for so we call it by the nature, the leaves in a bagg and Roots digged up with the earth about them in a

Rounlett.' (A rounlett was a small barrel.) Sir Nathaniel noted to himself: 'the poyson weed to blister withall'. As 'blistering' was used extensively by medical practitioners of the day to draw out what was poisoning the system presumably it was to be used for this. Michaux notes its presence in 1806 and Suzette Lloyd saw it in Walsingham in 1829, calling it 'poison weed'. She gives its Latin name as *Rhus radicans* and she found it in Somerset as well. She also mentions a 'poison tree'. There is no way of knowing if she meant the pencil tree — *Euphorbia tirucalli*.

POMEGRANATE
Punica granatum

They must have arrived very early in the colony for by 1617 Robert Rich was writing to Nathaniel about his house in a valley with a garden and an orchard already fenced in with figs and 'pommegraynoetts', and they were one of the fruits sent off to Virginia in 1621. An Act was passed in 1623 against the stealing of fruit and these were mentioned. It was intended that the road from Tucker's Town to King's Castle should be twelve feet wide and planted with figs and pomegranates — this in 1627 — but it remained an intention. However, like so much else, by 1687 Governor Robinson was writing that they had been blasted (by wind), and later Thomas Parsons in 1762 reported they had recovered and were one of the 'summer fruits'. Governor Hamilton saw them in 1790 and so did Suzette Lloyd in 1829. The value of the fruit was that the seeds were dried and eaten like nuts. The rind was used to prepare leather as it contains tannin and it also produces dyes — yellow, brown, or violet with different mordants. The old Bermuda remedy for labour pains was the bark boiled and the resulting tea drunk.

POTATO
Solanum tuberosum

The first potatoes seem to have arrived with Richard Moore's administration in 1612. Through carelessness the crop was nearly lost. However, the people quickly realised it could be a staple food and took more care after that. There are many references in the *Rich Papers* to them and Captain Smith said there were 'white, red and yellow' potatoes in 1623. Rents were paid in potatoes by 1638 and in 1639 the Spaniard confirms how many there were and how good. Although much else declined Governor Robinson in 1687 said potatoes were still being grown. Mark Catesby in 1714 declared: 'The Bermudas Potatoes is larger, rounder than the common . . .' Governor Hamilton in 1790 referred to 'Bermuda potatoes' too but young Wadsworth remarked in 1792, 'Though the finest Irish potatoes can be raised here . . . none which are not imported at five shillings to a dollar a bushel.' By 1829 things had improved again and Suzette Lloyd said 197 acres were devoted to potatoes. By 1844 the islands were producing 13,435 bushels and of that Smith's Parish was producing 3,705 bushels. They were still regarded as one of the principal products in 1868.

PRICKLY PEAR *Cactus opuntia*	Bermuda's only native cactus. It caused a great deal of interest at first as it was thought the cochineal insect might live on it. However, people discovered how good the fruit was to eat and Silvester Jourdan described in 1613 how a man ate more than a peck (two gallons) of them in ten hours and was none the worse for them. Robert Rich sent a basket of them to Nathaniel in 1617 but warned him to wait for Mr Day to show him how to eat them as they had 'a Burr in them, which you will hardly find unless he showes it unto you'. Very true. Norwood's *Journal* of 1616 has a good description of their way of growth and he describes how they were hung about store houses to preserve the corn from the rats and by the leaves dropping down new plants grew as further protection. By 1759 the plants were overhanging the enclosing walls of lots in St George's town and they were still there in 1806 when Michaux came. Suzette Lloyd commented on them in 1829 elsewhere in the island and by the nineteenth century a 'candy' was being made of them in St David's. According to Norwood the 'graynes' within the fruit were used for dyeing silk purple or scarlet, pink and salmon with different mordants, and finally they were supposed to cleanse the kidneys.
PRIDE OF INDIA *Melia azedarach* Chinaberry	A native of Persia it was introduced to America some time in the eighteenth century and from Charleston it was brought to Bermuda about 1780. Suzette Lloyd in 1829 said, 'Quay on Front Street planted with Pride of India' and she saw them at Walsingham. Michaux saw them in 1806. L.H. Smith has some other stories about the trees which are worth reading. They produce a khaki dye.
Prunus persica	Peach
Prunus sp.	Apricot
Psychotria ligustrifolia	Wild coffee
PUMPKIN *Cucurbita* sp.	The seeds must have been amongst those on the *Sea Venture* for when Richard Moore arrived in Bermuda in 1612 he found that the three men who had been left when the rest of the party went off to Virginia had planted and harvested 'numbers of pumpions ...'. Captain Smith in 1623 recorded them growing and an Act was passed the same year forbidding the stealing of them, amongst other fruits. They formed a staple part of the diet from then on, confirmed by household accounts of 1630. Thomas Parsons in 1762 declared: 'Seven months in the year we raise the best West India potatoes and pumpkins which the Inhabitants give preference to any kind of bread ...'
Punica granatum	Pomegranate

Queen of Shrubs
Lagestroemia indica

RADISH *Raphanus sativus*	It was a much prized medieval vegetable for its strong taste — like the onion family — so it is not surprising that it was one of the seeds sown by Sir George Somers in 1609 in his first garden. Captain John Smith reported in 1623 that there were 'exceeding large radishes'. No doubt they figured in both Thomas Parsons and Governor Hamilton's 'salletting'. They were eaten after meat as a digestive, and a syrup was made 'to provoke urine' and drive away the stone in the kidney according to Gerard. Samuel Pepys, the Diarist, was given the syrup after his bladder stone was removed in 1658.
Rhizophora mangle	Mangrove
RHUBARB *Rheum rhabarbarum*	The only person to mention this growing here is Governor Hamilton in 1790.
Rhus radicans	Mercury
Rhus toxicodendron	Poison ivy
Ricinus communis	Castor oil plant
ROSE *Rosa* sp.	It is hard for us to realise now the importance the rose had for previous generations, beautiful though we find them today. Fragrance was considered to be the breath of God on earth, hence the rose's holy and healing powers. Every part of the rose was used for different medicinal purposes — rosewater, conserves

and syrups were made. There are several references to rose stills in early accounts. The very earliest reference to there being roses here was by a Spaniard in 1639 and it would have been unthinkable for the people to have set out without them as the plant could travel easily. There is a list of medicaments bought in 1652 and half a pound of conserve of roses for three shillings is one. During the witchcraft trial in 1653 the suspected witch was made to smell a rose; no doubt the sweet smell was meant to confound her. Nathaniel Tucker mentions the 'blushing rose' in his poem of 1772 and young Wadsworth comments in 1792 'the Damask roses are in full bloom here'. Suzette Lloyd in 1829 points out there are 'no native roses' but lists several types growing.

ROSEMARY
Rosmarinus officinalis

There is no record of when this was imported but it may have been one of 'the sweet smelling herbs of the kind found in Spain' that the Spaniard saw in 1639. Governor Robinson says in 1687 that it was used for 'decking' and for favours at weddings. This in fact was an old English custom. It was planted on graves in the early eighteenth century. Mr W.E.S. Zuill in his *Bermuda Journey* has a lovely story about rosemary. It became naturalised in St David's and rosemary and molasses were boiled together to make a cough medicine, while rosemary alone was used as a hairwash.

Rubber Tree
Ficus elastica

Rubia tinctorum Madder

RUE
Ruta graveolens

It used to grow well in Somerset and it is a dye plant — dyeing red.

Rumex Dock

Sabal bermudana	Palmetto
Saccharum officinarum	Sugar

SAFFRON
Crocus sativus

This was a very important plant to people of earlier centuries. It was used a great deal in cooking and profusely mingled with medicines. The colour it conveyed seems to have been popular and it is one of the oldest dye plants. In England it was widely grown around Saffron Walden in Essex. Only the stamens of the crocus were used and it was a very labour-intensive crop. It was also a crop that impoverished the ground, the first year being the best — after three years something else had to be planted. After twenty years it could be grown again in the same spot. 'Warm nights, sweet dews, jet grounds, chiefly chalky, misty mornings are very good,' wrote one sixteenth century writer. There is in fact only one reference to it in Captain Smith's account of Bermuda in 1623 when he infers it may be a profitable crop — which it would if it had succeeded. The Richs did not refer to it at all. The amount of labour and the drying of the stamens would have presented a problem.

SAGE
Salvia sp.

No import date for this but as it has always been used when cooking pork it is likely to have arrived very early and it was growing in nineteenth century St David's.

Sagebush
Lantana involucrata

SAGO PALM
Cycas revoluta

Suzette Lloyd mentions this in 1829 and it was used as a centre for the turn around of drives to houses.

SALLETTING

A phrase used by both Thomas Parsons in 1762 and Governor Hamilton in 1790 without specifying exactly what they meant. There were simple and compound salads both served with oil and vinegar, the latter being a very elaborate mixture, the former being more what the modern salad is. A simple salad might consists of any of these — spring onions, chives, radishes, carrots, lettuce, purslane, samphire, asparagus, cucumbers or bean 'cods'.

Salix babylonica	Weeping willow
SALSIFY *Tragopogon* *porrifolius*	One of the vegetables entered in the first Agricultural Show in 1843.
Sambucus sp.	Elder
SARSAPARILLA *Smilax ornata*	True sarsaparilla comes from vines that are native to Central and South America. Originally taken to Spain in the sixteenth century it became a remedy for syphilis and later for rheumatic and dermatological complaints. Finally it was recognised as being merely of tonic and flavouring value. A plant of the same family was used in North America in the eighteenth century. Governor Hamilton noted just 'Sarsparilla' amongst his herbs and shrubs in 1790. However in 1846 the Virginia creeper — *Parthenocissus quinquefolia* was brought to Bermuda and according to Reade it was this plant that was used for sarsaparilla locally.
SCARLET CORDIA *Cordia sebestena*	Suzette Lloyd notes its presence in 1829. In the Bahamas it has a medicinal use — for sharpening the appetite.
SEA LAVENDER *Limonium* *carolinianum*	A native plant of Bermuda. Suzette Lloyd saw it in 1829 and gave its Latin name as *Heliotropium gnaphaloides*.
SHADDOCK *Citrus maxima*	Is the ancestor of our grapefruit, named after Captain Shaddock who had brought them from the East Indies. Governor Hamilton noted them in 1790 and so did Suzette Lloyd in 1829.
SHELL PLANT *Alpinia zerumbet*	One of the plants entered at the first Agricultural Show in 1843 according to Governor Reid.
Sida carpinfolia [Britton]	Wireweed
SILK COTTON TREE *Ceiba pentandra*	According to Britton two trees were planted at Mount Langton (Government House) by Governor Reid in 1845 but the Cox family at Orange Valley say their tree was brought from the West Indies by William John Cox about 1800 or 1820. However, as the Orange Valley one was smaller in 1914 when Britton observed it, it is a matter of speculation — perhaps it may be something to do with depth of soil and water.
Sisyrinchium *bermudiana*	Bermudiana

Smyrnium olusatrum	Alexanders
Solanum tuberosum	Potato
Solidago sempervirens	Golden rod
SORGHUM (or Guinea corn)	Observed growing by Suzette Lloyd in 1829.
Spanish bayonet	*Yucca aliofolia*
SPIDER LILY *Hymenocallis declinata*	This grows wild in Bermuda and we have no import date for it but it had a medicinal use in old Bermuda — the root was used against blood poisoning.
SPINACH *Spinacia oleracea*	First noted by Governor Hamilton in 1790 amongst his list of vegetables.
Steriotaphrum secondatum	Crab grass
STOPPER *Eugenia axillaris*	A native plant. In Norwood's remarks and description of Bermuda in 1616 he lists the trees that they found when they arrived. He says, 'The country when we first began the Plantation was all over grown with Woods and Plants of several kinds and to such gave names, such as were known retaining their old names; as Cedars, Palmetoes . . . Stopper-trees . . .' It is interesting that the plant was recognised for what it was. In the Bahamas it is used as a remedy for 'building up men's energy and body' and as a sponge bath 'after coming out of straw bed', i.e. after childbirth.
STRAWBERRY *Fragaria*	First mentioned by Governor Hamilton in 1790 and seen again by Suzette Lloyd in 1829.
SUGAR APPLE *Anona squamosa*	A native of tropical America it was first noted by Suzette Lloyd in 1829 and a drawing of it also appears in a collection of about 1882.
SUGAR *Saccharum officinarum*	Sugar arrived in Europe from the Far East during the time of the Crusades. Sweetness was also provided by things like honey, currants and verjuice during earlier centuries. In 1616 Daniel Tucker received instructions from the Company to obtain sugar-canes from the West Indies and later the same year the *Edwin* arrived with them. A parcel of canes were sent to Virginia in

1619 for experimental planting but the crop failed. Bermuda proved to be too rocky and dry according to the early settlers although the rainfall did appear to be sufficient. However the crop must have flourished to a certain extent because in the ship of presents sent to Virginia in 1619 sugar-canes were included. Captain Smith commented in 1626 that there was an abundance of sugar-canes and sugar was being made. The truth seems to be contained in a letter dated 1625 from the Company to Captain Woodhouse which says that though sugar-cane was planted at their orders, the settlers had reaped it before it was properly ripe so that it was only fit for pigs, the reason being they were more interested in growing tobacco. However in 1669 there is an entry in the Virginia Company journal: 'ingenious endeavor of Captain Hubbard promoting planting of sugar in Somers Isles . . .' and a box of sugar had been sent. They sent him an Anchor of Brandy they were so pleased. They also pointed out if there were objections to the making of sugar because it meant cutting cedar trees for burning then coal could be sent. They were right because in 1675 a law did have to be passed prohibiting the burning of cedar in the manufacture of sugar. However in 1712 46 tons were entered in the Customs House records in England as having come from Bermuda. By 1735 though an Act was passed to encourage planting of sugar-cane. There were still plantations in Somerset by 1829 but by 1858 sugar was to be found 'in gardens only'. The 'Sugar and spice' asked for in the *Rich Papers* is in fact a mixture of exactly that obtained from grocers already mixed for use in cooking.

Suriana maritima	Tassel plant

SURINAM CHERRY
Eugenia uniflora

A native of South America. Governor Hamilton in 1790 mentions 'cherries' and 'sherries'. Whether this is a slip of the pen or he meant two different fruits we shall never know. By 1840 there was a Surinam cherry tree at Orange Valley; it was mentioned in an inventory of the estate. It must have been planted in the early 1800s.

SWEET POTATO
Ipomoea batatas

The sweet potato was discovered in South America at very much the same time as the 'Irish' potato. Although there are many references to potatoes in the early years and it is highly likely they arrived with the other plants on the *Edwin* from the West Indies in 1616, the first proper reference to 'sweet potatoes' is by the shipwrecked Spaniard in 1639 when he says, 'Potatoes are very large, eaten many [sweet potatoes] more than two pounds each, good taste and flavour'. Thomas Parsons in 1762 refers to the 'West Indian potato' which he says are produced for seven months of the year. Governor Hamilton mentions both kinds in

1790 calling these Spanish potatoes but adds, 'Two of these cut into quarters which were planted on the 19th of last December and taken up the 28th March 1790 were found to have produced 113 potatoes, the largest weighing 5 ounces each of which were 36, the smallest one ounce each.' By 1844 Bermuda was producing 11,269 bushels, of which Sandys parish produced 4,614 bushels alone. They had a medicinal use as well — eaten raw as quickly as possible and by drinking plenty of milk they were an antidote for mackerel poisoning.

SWORD TREE
Erythrina
corallodendron

This tree was discovered in the Cape region of South Africa by Francis Masson soon after 1773. In 1829 Suzette Lloyd, calling it the coral tree, says, 'no more than eight or nine feet high' but she gave it the correct Latin name.

Symphytum
officinale

Comfrey

TAMARIND
Tamarindus indica

There is a tradition in Bermuda that Tamarind trees were planted near the family burying grounds. Certainly there is one at Orange Grove which, when planted, was near the 'smooth-wall garden'. The tree is still there and there is one near the Hayward graveyard in Emily Bay Lane, St David's. That one is very much the same size as the one at Waterville, Paget, which is thought to have been planted about 1711. The one at Emily Bay Lane was cut down to make a gun-carriage many years ago and what is there now is the re-growth. Governor Hamilton mentions them in 1790 and Suzette Lloyd saw them in Warwick in 1829.

TAMARISK
Tamarix gallica

It was Governor Reid's suggestion in 1839 that this should be planted along the North Shore road to provide shelter.

TANSY
Tanacetum vulgare

Tansy was certainly growing in St David's in the nineteenth century and when Captain Fred Virtue went to sea in May 1864 as the ship's boy he was given 'a little bottle of Rum and tansie that was for me when I got seasick'. Tansy in port wine was for upset stomachs and it grew well 'in yards' I am told. It is a fly repellent and a dye plant, giving green from the root and yellow from the leaves.

Taraxacum officinale   Dandelion

TASSEL PLANT
Suriana maritima   A native of Bermuda, Suzette Lloyd remarked on it growing along the sea shore in 1829.

Terminalia catappa   West Indian almond

THISTLE
Mexican poppy thistle
Argemone mexicana   Suzette Lloyd said in 1829 that it was used to dye ribbons yellow. In the Bahamas the juice of the broken stem is used to cure ringworm and warts and a tea made of the whole to cure hepatitis.

Thornapple
Jimson weed
Datura stramonium and *Datura tatula*.

THYME
Thymus sp.   Growing in St David's in the nineteenth century although we have no import date.

TOBACCO
Nicotiana tabacum   It is difficult for us today to comprehend the importance that tobacco had in the economy of seventeenth century Bermuda. It was used as currency, for rents and men were paid in it; it seems to have been the largest single crop for some years. The very earliest account of it growing is that by the Spanish in 1603 when they found a patch 'growing as though planted by man'. Certainly the three men left on Bermuda at the departure of the *Deliverance* and the *Patience* for Virginia subsequently grew it, according to Silvester Jourdan. The Inspectors of tobacco were sworn in to their posts, which were obviously considered to be important and trustworthy for there are accounts of tobacco being incorrectly cured and therefore, when packed, spoiling the rest. It was still being grown in the early eighteenth century but, like so much else, in smaller quantities. Governor Bennett in 1703 declared that not much more was grown than used by the family — 'some familys smoke 200 cwt.' and 'quantity of tobacco yearly smoked about 50,000 weight'. The decline was due to two factors. One — originally land was inhabited by tenants who grew tobacco and paid rents in it; later the inhabitants were freeholders and preferred to grow cedar for shipbuilding. Two — the duty on tobacco was raised and profits went down. By 1829 Suzette Lloyd saw it still growing in Somerset but by 1868 it was just growing wild.

TOMATO	A native of South America and brought to England in the
Lycopersicon	sixteenth century. Gerard in 1596 calls it 'Apples of Love' and
	describes both the red and yellow tomato. He says it grows in
	hot countries such as Spain and Italy and describes how it is
	cooked as a sauce for meat as well as eaten with oil and vinegar.
	It may well have come to Bermuda earlier but the first mention
	of it is when ten boxes were exported in 1851.

| *Tragopogon* | Salsify |
| *porrifolius* | |

| *Triticum* | Wheat |

| *Tropaeolum* | Nasturtium |

Turk's cap cactus
Melocactus
  communis

TURNIP	The first mention of turnips growing in Bermuda at all is in 1844
Brassica rapa	when 657 bushels were grown and of that Smith's Parish grew
	305 bushels.

| URTICA | Nettle |

92

Vigna unguiculata	Blackeyed pea
VINES *Vitis*	The 'Authorities' in England were convinced during the first two hundred years of Bermuda's history that grapes should grow, in spite of evidence to the contrary. Daniel Tucker was sent cuttings in 1616 with explicit instructions as to cultivation and he had his own vineyard on the Overplus at Port Royal. Robert Rich planted them in his garden in 1617 but there were repeated requests for a 'vignerone' to be sent to assist with the cultivation as the grapes failed to ripen and became diseased. Help never was sent and the planters complained that vines took up too much space. The Company remained unconvinced and wrote somewhat plaintively to Woodhouse in 1625 that surely if figs would grow, vines should, and that a little application to the problems was needed. The shipwrecked Spaniard declared in 1639 that there were 'many vineyards'. Governor Bruere planted grapes north of St George's in 1765 and by 1781 some Bermuda wine was made, although when it was served at a dinner party for the Governor on Cooper's Island it was not considered to be very good. In 1785 the Assembly set a maximum price on wine to try to encourage the cultivation of vines. Governor Hamilton in 1790 merely noted there were grapes. Suzette Lloyd's comment in 1829 was that earlier many, many grapes had been grown at Tucker's Town but not by then.
VIRGINIA CREEPER *Parthenocissus* *quinquefolia*	In 1846 according to the *Royal Gazette* a new plant was brought to Bermuda and did well. See the story about sarsaparilla under that listing.
Vitex agnus *castus*	Chaste tree

WATER LEMON Yellow granadilla *Passiflora laurifolia*	Bell-Apple Suzette Lloyd lists this amongst her fruits of 1829.
WATER-MELON *Citrullus lanatus*	Captain Smith lists these as one of the good and successful plants of 1623. Thomas Parsons lists them as a summer fruit in 1762 and Governor Hamilton saw them in 1790.
WEEPING WILLOW *Salix babylonica*	Collinson said it came from the Euphrates and was first imported into England in 1748. Suzette Lloyd saw it growing here in 1829.
WHEAT *Triticum*	In Silvester Jourdan's letter of 1612 he comments that the three men left on Bermuda after the departure of the *Deliverance* and the *Patience* for Virginia had a 'great store of wheate' by that date. Governor Hamilton refers in 1790 to 'Red Wheat'. In both cases the men writing meant 'wheat' rather than 'corn' which they referred to as either 'corn' or 'Indian corn'.
WIREWEED *Sida carpinfolia* [Britton]	The first mention of this tough plant is when Governor Heydon made an Order to pull up wireweed in 1669. Governor Robinson complained in 1687 that the wireweed was very bad. It was collected by Revd Clerk as a curiosity for his collection of plants in 1734. It had its medicinal uses — either crushed for bee stings or applied as a poultice.

YAMS *Dioscorea*	The only mention of these is by Governor Hamilton in 1790 in his list of *Roots*.
YELLOW WOOD *Zanthoxylum flavum*	One of Bermuda's endemic plants. It caused a lot of interest and comment by the first people to arrive. It was valued for both its colour and hardness. By 1632 it was necessary to forbid the destruction and waste of it together with other woods.
YUCCA Spanish bayonet *Yucca aliofolio*	A native of Bermuda. There seems to have been some confusion over the name of this plant and its uses in the seventeenth century. In 1639 the shipwrecked Spaniard wrote that in each little farm was planted with 'yucca for making cassava flour'. Gerard in his *Herbal* of 1597 makes the same mistake but it is corrected by Thomas Johnson in his new edition of the *Herbal* in 1633. He points out that true cassava comes from another plant and his description makes it clear he knew which one. In 1829 Suzette Lloyd saw 'thick fences' of it in Somerset.

Zanthoxylum flavum	Yellow wood
Zea mays	Corn — Maize
Zingiber officinalis	Ginger

Dates of importation of plants to Bermuda

In accordance with the idea set out in *Plants of Colonial Williamsburg* by Joan Parry Dutton, 1979, the dates are usually the first mention of the plant in question. It is possible they were tried before, failed and were re-introduced satisfactorily at or by this date.

1593	Pawpaw	Olives	
1609	Fig	'Kitchen herbs'	Onions
	Peas	Musk-melons	Lettuce
	Radish		
1610	Beans	Mulberry	Corn(Wheat)
	Carrots	Tobacco	Melons
	Cucumber	Beets	Parsnips
1613	Potatoes	Pumpkins	
1615	Citron	Grape vines	
1616	Anise	Pomegranates	Limes
	Cassava	Sugar-cane	Oranges
	Lemons	Basil	Plantains
	Marjoram	Fennel	Sweet potato
	Pineapples		
1623	Artichoke	Water-melon	Castor oil
	Bird pepper		
1624	Indigo (dye plant)	Wild indigo	
	Madder	*Baptisia tinctoria*	
	Curron vines	Saffron	
		Cotton	
1632	Flax	Hemp	
	Bananas		
1639	Rose		
1669	Bermudiana (mentioned)		
1671	Guava		
1678	*Datura stramonium*	*Datura tatula*	
1687	Rosemary		
Some time in the 17th century	*Cactus melocactus*	Date palm	

1711	Tamarind		
1734	'small hibiscus' Lantana	Mahogany	
1748	Locust tree (*Hymenaea courbaril*)		
1763	Calabash		
1772	Myrtle Nasturtiums Jasmine	Honeysuckle Vitex (Chaste tree) Carnation	*Poinciana pulcherrima*
1777	Begonia		
1780	Pride of India (Melia azerdarach)		
1790	Oleander Arrowroot Surinam cherry Shaddock Peach	Rhubarb Ipecacuanha Aloe Coffee Lavender	Strawberries Granadilla Sarsaparilla *Yucca gloriosa*
1806	Geraniums, zonal and roseum		
1813	Floppers		
1819	*Lantana camara*		
1825	*Hibiscus tiliaceus*		
1826	Sword tree — *Erythina corallodendron* *Ficus elastica*		
1829	*Hibiscus mutabilis* Almond Althea Sago palm Sugar apple	Water lemon Arabian jessamine Passion flower Mamee apple	Weeping willow Avocado Scarlet cordia Golden Shower
1830	Fiddlewood		
1839	Tamarisk		
1843	*Colla Ethiopica* *Fuschia grandiflora*	Shell plant Brugmanzia	*Fuschia globosa* Dahlia
1845	Balsam of Peru	Silk cotton tree	
1846	Virginia creeper	Breadfruit	
1856	Poinsettia	Loquat	Easter lily
By this date	Tansy Mint	Horehound Mullein	

Chronological list of events in Bermuda

1603	Description of what they found by Spaniards who landed.
1609	The arrival of the *Sea Venture* after the hurricane.
1610	The departure of the newly built *Patience* and the *Deliverance* for Virginia.
1612	Arrival of the first colonists on *The Plough* with Governor Richard Moore.
1613	Sylvester Jourdan's account sent home from Bermuda to London.
1615	The first of the correspondence known as the *Rich Papers*, which continued for thirty years.
1616	Norwood's first survey.
1619	The start of Captain John Smith's account of Virginia and Bermuda.
1620	The first elected House of Assembly met on August 1st. Acts passed regulating boundaries, their maintenance and replanting and the control of turkey flocks.
1631	Norwood's map printed by John Speed, on the back of which was an excerpt of his Journal.
1638	14th February. Provision in a lease that if the tobacco crop destined for rent payment were blown away then rent could be paid the following year — typical provision in several leases.
1639	The shipwrecked Spaniard's account.
1644	9th June. An agreement stating 'said Mr. Watlington doe with his owne hands weave twenty yards of brode linen cloth' and the apprenticeship of Elizabeth Pitcher to Ralph Wright of Longbird Island as a weaver.
1647	'Joyner' mentioned as one of trades.
1648	10th August. A carpenter's rent for an acre of land 'a coople of capons as a New Year's gift'.
1649	A negro 'boatwright' mentioned. At about this time mentions of trading with the West Indian islands of Barbados, Barbuda and Montserrat and St Christopher's (St Kitts), and Indian slaves were as numerous as negroes.

1650	31st January. As rent, oranges and lemons packed in cedar boards and potatoes put in cedar cask for dispatch to England.
1652	The King of Poland stayed in Bermuda from 1652–55. His surgeon provided medicaments one of which was '½lb of conserve of roses at three shillings'.
1653	Captain Burrows paid one pound and two shillings for a rose-still and a 'chirurgeon' and 'taylor' are mentioned. A rose is given to a supposed witch at her trial. In the inventory of Thomas Durham's will (who was a tenant of the Rich's) there appears a buttery, a separate 'milkhouse' and shoemaking equipment. The word Virginia was spelt as it was said 'Wirginia'.
1656	Captain Jennings rented to Gideon and William Sears 25 acres for which they paid 220lbs of tobacco, 2 capons, a turkeycock, 200 oranges and 200 weight of potatoes. John Dorrell paid to Robert Collinsone for a bill of £181 12s 3d. fresh beef, fresh pork, butter and 3,000 fish.
1658	Letter from Barbados asking for fennel seed. 18th February. Of a list of things to go to England 'one small cedar desk and 3,840 sticks Brazilletta wood'. For contravening a lease by cutting down orange and fig trees the culprit must make 'Mrs Burroes a desk'. Norwood's second survey.
1660	Stephen Paynter (another Rich tenant) had a 'Big house, two lofts, lots of little outbuildings, a stillhouse and one rose-still'.
1669	From an entry in the Virginia Company Journal: 'For the ingenious endeavor of Captain J. Hubbard in promoting the planting of sugar-cane in Somers Islands' he was sent an anchor of brandy (they were so pleased) followed by comment coal could be sent if there was not enough wood for preparing sugar.
1675	Law passed prohibiting the burning of cedar in manufacture of sugar.
1684	The Bermuda Company ceased to exist.
1687	Bermuda received Sir Robert Robinson as first royal governor. 11th June Robinson's letter to Secretary for Trade and Plantations giving very good description of the islands and the people. Of the 579 houses only 29 had stone roofs, the remainder would have been palmetto thatched.
1699	John Dickinson started to despatch his collections of plants to James Petiver of London.
1700	The start of regular correspondence by Governors to Secretary of State for Trade and Plantations about state of Bermuda's agriculture and poverty.

In Richard Parker's will were listed nine old cedar beehives and a pestle and mortar.

1701	John Lawson's book *A new Voyage to Carolina* in which he describes the Bermuda sloops trading.
1705	Cedars beginning to grow again and being used for shipbuilding. Importation of food. Making and export of 'plait'.
1706	Trade with West Indies and carrying of salt to New England. Ships returning with food of every kind and clothes. Tobacco cultivation declined so much it was imported from Virginia.
1712	Entry in English Customs House records that 46 tons of sugar came from Bermuda.
1714	Mark Catesby's possible visit to Bermuda.
1722	John Hope arrived as Governor. Act passed to halt destruction of palmettoes and to prevent fraud in measuring of 'plait'.
1730	Governor Pitt's descriptions of small amount of food produced locally, only onions exported and emigration of 2,000 people because of poverty.
1734	Revd William Clerk visited collecting plants.
1735	Council's Report to the House of Lords on state of Bermuda and Governor Pitt's report to Council describing decline in 'plait' trade but export of produce and poultry.
1738	Governor Popple tried to encourage farming.
1740	The last sugar produced. Restriction of cattle export suggested.
1741	Other food exports prohibited.
1744	Smallpox arrived on ship out of Philadelphia.
1745	*Endeavour* from West Indies bound for Virginia wrecked with negroes on board.
1758	John Ellis wrote to Dr Garden, in Charleston, and referred to Bermuda.
1762	3rd November. Thomas Parson's account of Bermuda in letter to Sir Francis Dashwood.
1765	Governor Bruere's letter to Board of Trade. Emigration of people to East Florida because of poverty and distress.
1770	Trade by Bermuda vessels in mahogany and logwood from Honduras to England.
1772	John Ellis's *Botanical Tracts* published. Correspondence between members of Tucker family and composing of the poem 'The Bermudian'.
1773	Henry Tucker writing to St George Tucker of the 'starving condition' of the people.

1775	Col Henry Tucker's journey to America followed by the 'gunpowder steal'. Still great shortage of provisions. Trade in turtles to intercept East Indiamen at Ascension Island.
1776	American Revolution.
1778	Philip Freneau's account.
1780	Heavy toll of trees in great hurricane.
1781	Governor William Browne arrived. Accounts of lack of trade, partial famine and poverty since the American Revolution.
1784	Jean Crevecoeur's account.
1787	Dr Francis Forbes' account.
1788	Governor Henry Hamilton arrived.
1789	Trade in timber from Honduras to England still continuing. Start of French Revolution with its effects on islands in Caribbean.
1790	Governor Hamilton's account and plant list.
1792	Wadsworth letters.
1806	François André Michaux's account.
1829	The start of Harriet Suzette Lloyd's visit to Bermuda and her account.
1839	Governor William Reid's arrival and his correspondence.
1843	First Agricultural Show.
1844	'Return of Ground Productions' to be published in Williams' book.
1848	*An Historical and Statistical Account of the Bermudas* by William Frith Williams published; the first history of Bermuda.

Some plants grown in eighteenth century American gardens

THEY WILL GROW IN BERMUDA BUT WE HAVE NO IMPORTATION DATE.

Allysum
Antirrinhum
Aquilegia
Aristolochia
(Dutchman's pipe)
Aster
Balsam
(Impatiens)
Bignonia capreolata
Campsis radicans
Trumpet vine
Camomile
Candytuft
Canna indica
Cineraria
Dusty Miller
Chrysanthemum
(various plants under this name)
Coreopsis
Day lily
Dianthus
Elder
Gallardia
Gardenia
Garlic
Globe amaranth
Golden rod
Helichrysum

Heliotrope
Hollyhock
Iceplant
(Mesembryanthemum)
Iris
Ivy
Laurestinus
Viburnum tinus
Larkspur
Lobelia
Magnolia
Marvel of Peru
Nigella damascena
Pansy
Periwinkle
Phlox
Poppy
Portulaca
Sweet pea
Santolina
Scabious
Spider lily (*Hymenocallis*)
Statice
Stocks
Sunflower
Sweet William
Yarrow
Zinnia

N.B. Lefroy wrote a chapter in a book *Naturalist in Bermuda* edited by J.M. Jones. Lefroy's chapter was 'Botany' and in it he gives a very good list of what was growing by 1875. I suggest that book is consulted for after 1850.

Bibliography

Alicia Amherst *A History of Gardening in England* 1896

Bermuda Garden 1955 published by The Garden Club of Bermuda

Bermuda Historical Quarterly 1947–1979

Mrs William Bluck *Diary* 1860 by kind permission of Mr John Cox

N.L. Britton *Flora of Bermuda* 1918 Charles Scribener

Arthur Bryant *Man in the Making* Samuel Pepys' Diaries 1954 Collins

Calendar of State Papers, Colonial Series, America and West Indies 1700–35

Mark Catesby *Natural History of Carolina, Florida and the Bahama Islands* 1771 Edition

Noel Deerr *The History of Sugar* 1947

Colin Dence *Herbal Review Classic Herb and Spice Recipes* 1981–85

John Dickinson *Letters* 1700 Sloane Manuscripts, British Museum 4063 ff 14, 33, 63

John Ellis *Botanical Tracts* 1772 Massachussetts Horticultural Library C.41 E 472d.

Sarah Garland *Herb and Spice Book* 1979 Weidenfeld and Nicholson

John Gerard *The Herbal* Revised by Thomas Johnson 1633 Reprint Constable & Co. 1975

Richard Gorer *Flower Garden in England* 1975 B.T. Batsford

Henry Hamilton *Of the Soils and Productions of Bermuda* 1790 by kind permission of the Houghton Library, Harvard University

Dorothy Hartley *The Land of England* 1979 Macdonald General Books

Mrs L. Higgs *Bush Medicine in the Bahamas* 1969 Nassau Guardian

John Hope *Private Letter Book, 1722–29* MS Rawlinson A.484 by kind permission of the Bodleian Library, Oxford

W.B. Kerr *Bermuda and the American Revolution 1760–83* 1936 Princeton University Press

Norma Jean Lathrop *Herbs* H.P. Books, Tucson Arizona

John Lawson *A New Voyage to Carolina* 1701

Major-General J.H. Lefroy, C.B., F.R.S., R.A. *Memorials of the Discovery and Early Settlement of the Bermudas or Somers Islands 1515–1685*, 2 vols   London 1877 and 1879   Reprint University of Toronto Press 1981 funded by Bermuda National Trust

Ann Leighton *American Gardens in the Eighteenth Century*

1976   Houghton Mifflin Co. Boston, Mass.

Ann Leighton   *Early American Gardens*   1970   Houghton Mifflin Co. Boston, Mass.

Harriet Suzette Lloyd   *Sketches of Bermuda*   1835   James Cochrane, London by kind permission of the Bermuda Archives

Teresa McLean   *Medieval English Gardens*   1981   Collins

François André Michaux *Notice sur les Iles Bermudes et particulièrement sur L'Ile Saint Georges* Annales du Muséum d'Histoire Naturelle, Paris 1806

Natural Plant Dyeing   Brooklyn Botanic Garden Record, Vol 29, No. 2.

Philip Miller   *Gardeners' Dictionary*   1769

Thomas Parsons   *Letter to Sir Francis Dashwood*   1762   *Dashwood Papers* MS.

DD Dashwood b. 7/l by kind permission of Sir Francis Dashwood   Bodleian Library, Oxford

Governor Reid   *Personal Papers*   1839   by kind permission of the Bermuda Archives

Louisa Hutchings Smith   *Bermuda's Oldest Inhabitants, Tales of Plant Life*   1950   Revised edition 1963   by kind permission of Mrs A.Tompkins

The Rich Papers Letters from Bermuda 1615–1646 Edited by Vernon Ives University of Toronto Press 1984 funded by Bermuda National Trust

Nathaniel Tucker *The Bermudian* 1772 Reprinted Bermuda National Trust 1983

Daniel Wadsworth   *Letters*   1792   B.H.Q. 1958

Henry Wilkinson *Bermuda in the Old Empire* 1950 Oxford University Press

William Frith Williams   *An Historical and statistical account of The Bermudas*   1848

W.S. Zuill   *Bermuda Sampler*   1937   Richard Clay & Sons

W.S. Zuill   *The Story of Bermuda and Her People*   1973   Macmillan

Unpublished documents on early Colonial Records in the Bermuda Archives